HANDS-ON ABCs

ABC Art

by Marilynn G. Barr

50806

Publisher: Roberta Suid

Production: Little Acorn & Associates, Inc.

MM2191
ABC ART

For a complete catalog, write to the address below:
Monday Morning Books, Inc.
PO Box 1134
Inverness, CA 94937

Call our toll-free number: 1-800-255-6049
E-mail us at: MMBooks@aol.com
Visit our Web site:
http://www.mondaymorningbooks.com

ISBN 1-57612-217-4

Printed in the United States of America
9 8 7 6 5 4 3 2 1

Contents

Introduction

ABC Art is one of four Hands-on ABC books (*ABC Scissor Skills*, *ABC Mini Books*, and *ABC Games*) designed to provide alphabet skills practice activities for early learners. Children practice recognizing letters and letter sounds and associating letters with alphabet pictures. These activities also offer early skills practice such as coloring, cutting, gluing, folding, and lacing while fostering individual creativity.

Reproduce the Pattern and Picture Squares on pages 10-61 for children to make alphabet finger paintings, craft stick projects, wallpaper puzzles, collages, mobiles, garlands, lacing cards, alphabet pillows, folders and scrapbooks. Pattern and Picture Squares include an alphabet picture pattern, alphabet picture squares, and large, outline upper- and lowercase letters for each letter of the alphabet.

Prepare a workstation with the materials listed below for a creative alphabet skills practice center.

Materials List

construction paper
oak tag
folders
crayons
markers
scissors
finger-painting paper
finger paints
craft sticks
wallpaper scraps
pom poms
glitter
cotton balls
beads
beans
yarn
elbow macaroni (uncooked)
rice (uncooked)
popcorn (popped and unpopped)
buttons
glue
stapler

Alphabet Collages

Reproduce oak tag letter and alphabet patterns for children to create alphabet collages. Provide a variety of craft materials for children to glue onto letter boards and alphabet picture patterns. Children can glue lengths of yarn to decorate letters and pattern pictures or craft materials that begin with matching letters such as buttons on Bb, cotton balls on Cc, popcorn on Pp. A list of matching letter craft materials is listed below. Alphabet picture squares, letter squares pp. 62-64), or cutouts from magazines such as eggs for Ee and kites for Kk can also be used to glue onto letters or picture patterns when a matching letter craft material is not available. Help each child write his or her name on the collage. Then mount finished collages on a display board.

Matching Letter Craft Materials

Aa acorns, matching alphabet picture and letter squares
Bb buttons, beans, beads, matching alphabet picture and letter squares
Cc cotton balls, matching alphabet picture and letter squares
Dd sticker dots, matching alphabet picture and letter squares
Ee wiggle eyes, matching alphabet picture and letter squares
Ff artificial flowers, feathers, matching alphabet picture and letter squares
Gg glitter, grass, matching alphabet picture and letter squares
Hh heart stickers, matching alphabet picture and letter squares
Ii matching alphabet picture and letter squares
Jj matching alphabet picture and letter squares
Kk toy keys, matching alphabet picture and letter squares
Ll leaves, matching alphabet picture and letter squares
Mm matching alphabet picture and letter squares
Nn small nuts, matching alphabet picture and letter squares
Oo cereal Os, matching alphabet picture and letter squares
Pp pom poms, popped popcorn, matching alphabet picture and letter squares
Qq quilt squares, matching alphabet picture and letter squares
Rr rice, matching alphabet picture and letter squares
Ss sequins, snowflake stickers, star stickers, matching alphabet picture and letter squares
Tt triangles, matching alphabet picture and letter squares
Uu matching alphabet picture and letter squares
Vv matching alphabet picture and letter squares
Ww plastic fishing worms, matching alphabet picture and letter squares
Xx matching alphabet picture and letter squares
Yy yarn scraps, matching alphabet picture and letter squares
Zz zippers, matching alphabet pictures and letters

Craft Stick Alphabet Art

Prepare a work station with the following materials:

- construction paper alphabet pattern and picture squares
- crayons or markers
- scissors
- craft sticks
- glue

Have children choose, then color and cut out an alphabet pattern. Then help each child glue a craft stick to the back of his or her alphabet pattern.

Wallpaper Alphabet Puzzles

Reproduce and cut apart wallpaper alphabet pattern and picture squares to form puzzles. Store each puzzle in a separate resealable plastic bag. Children can work on one or more puzzles individually or in pairs. Store Wallpaper Alphabet Puzzles in a decorated shoe box.

Alphabet Garlands

Reproduce a set of colored construction paper alphabet picture squares for each child to cut apart. Then help each child glue his or her set of squares onto a length of yarn. Write children's names on the backs of alphabet squares. When the glue has dried, display each child's alphabet garland on the bulletin board. Or tape garlands onto children's desks.

Alphabet Finger Painting

Cover a table with newspaper and provide smocks, finger-painting paper, finger paints, and paper towels for children to create Alphabet Finger Paintings. Choose, then reproduce construction paper alphabet pictures for children to cut out and glue onto their paintings. Help each child write his or her name on the painting. Mount finished paintings on separate sheets of colored construction paper. Review the list below for finger-painting suggestions.

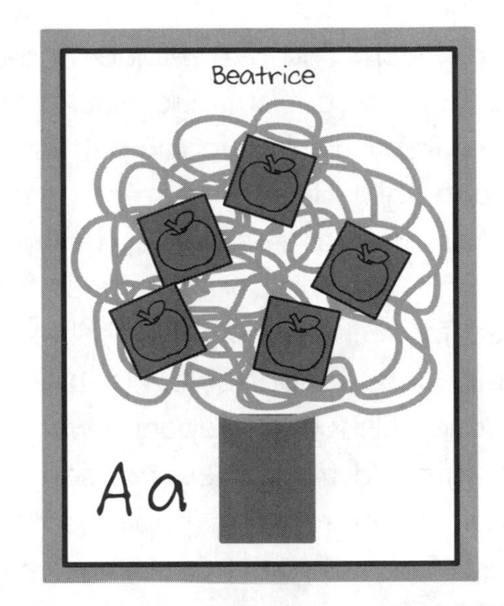

Finger-painting Suggestions

Aa finger-paint a tree, glue on apple squares
Bb finger-paint a nest, glue on bird squares
Cc finger-paint a road, glue on car cards
Dd finger-paint a grassy field, glue on dog cards
Ee finger-paint a basket, glue on egg cards
Ff finger-paint a fish bowl, glue on fish cards
Gg finger-paint a night sky, glue on ghost squares
Hh finger-paint a blue sky, glue on hot air balloon squares
Ii finger-paint a mountain, glue on igloo squares
Jj finger-paint a jar, glue on jack squares
Kk finger-paint a kite with a tail, glue on key squares
Ll finger-paint a leaf, glue on ladybug squares
Mm finger-paint a piece of cheese, glue on mice squares
Nn finger-paint a tree with branches, glue on nest squares
Oo finger-paint a pine tree, glue on ornament squares
Pp finger-paint a garden, glue on pumpkin squares
Qq finger-paint a bed, glue on quilt squares
Rr finger-paint a dark sky, glue on raindrop squares
Ss finger-paint an ocean, glue on sailboat squares
Tt finger-paint a field, glue on tree squares
Uu finger-paint a rainy sky, glue on umbrella squares
Vv finger-paint a sandy beach, glue on volleyball squares
Ww finger-paint an ocean, glue on whale squares
Xx finger-paint simple music notes, glue on xylophone squares
Yy finger-paint a toy box, glue on yo-yo squares
Zz finger-paint a sweater, glue on zipper squares

Alphabet Lacing Cards

Reproduce, color, cut out, and laminate alphabet pattern and picture squares. Use a hole punch to punch an even number of holes around the edge of each pattern to form alphabet lacing cards. Measure and cut a length of yarn to fit each pattern for children to practice lacing. Store alphabet lacing cards and yarn in separate resealable plastic bags. Place the bags in a basket or decorated shoe box.

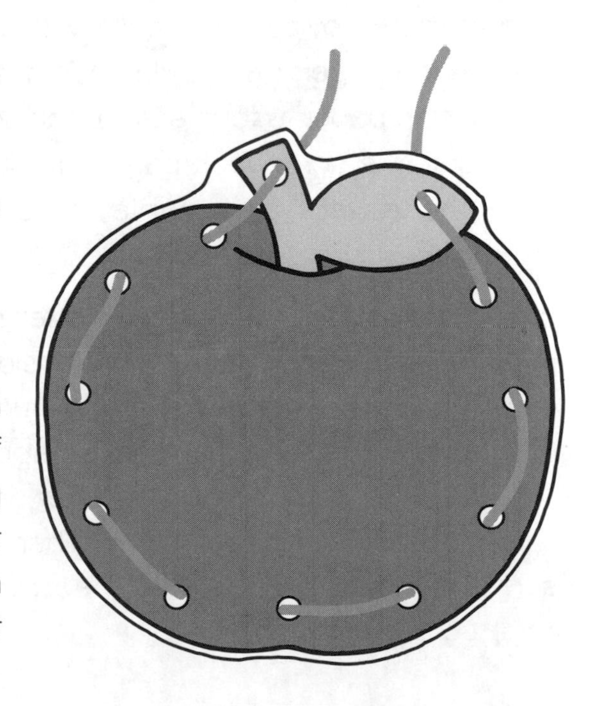

Alphabet Folders and Scrapbooks

Alphabet Folders

Provide each child with a folder and a letter board. Have children color, cut out, and glue letter boards onto their folders. Reproduce matching pattern and picture squares for each child. Have children color, cut out, and glue the patterns and squares to the inside of their folders. Help each child write his or her name on the front of the folder. Repeat for each letter of the alphabet. Store finished folders in a decorated portable file box or an alphabetical accordion file folder. Prepare a work station with baskets filled with old magazines, coupon and sale flyers, and sheets of construction paper to fit inside of alphabet folders. Each child chooses one of his or her alphabet folders to work with. At the work station, children look through magazines, cut out, and glue pictures that match the letter on their folders onto a sheet of construction paper. Sheets are then stored inside folders.

Alphabet Scrapbooks

Provide each child with two sheets of construction paper, one letter board and matching alphabet pattern and picture squares. Have children color, cut out, and glue the letter board and patterns on two separate sheets of construction paper to form scrapbook pages. Store completed pages in separate folders labeled with children's names. When children have made scrapbook pages for each letter of the alphabet, provide each child with a large sheet of construction paper. Have children fold and decorate the construction paper to form scrapbook covers. Help each child insert the scrapbook pages, in alphabetical order, inside the covers and staple to form an Alphabet Scrapbook.

Children can also form individual-letter scrapbooks with the alphabet picture sheets stored inside their alphabet folders. Provide each child with a construction paper folder to decorate for an individual letter scrapbook cover. Have each child write the appropriate letter on the front of his or her construction paper cover. Then help each child insert his or her pages inside the cover and staple to form a scrapbook.

Alphabet Mobiles

Design 1

Reproduce an oak tag alphabet letter set (letter board, matching pattern, and picture squares strip) for each child to make an Alphabet Mobile. Have children color and cut out their letter boards, matching patterns, and pictures squares strips. (Do not cut picture squares apart.) Cut a length of yarn to accommodate the letter board, picture squares strip, and pattern for each child. Then help each child glue or staple the yarn length to the back of his or her letter board, strip, and pattern. Hang completed Alphabet Mobiles from the ceiling or on a display board.

Design 2

Reproduce an oak tag letter board and matching pattern for each child. Also enlarge, reproduce, and provide children with picture squares to make Alphabet Mobiles. Have children color and cut out their letter boards, matching patterns, and enlarged pictures squares. Help children measure and cut yarn lengths to glue or staple to the backs of patterns and picture squares. Then help each child attach (glue or staple) the pattern and picture squares to the bottom of his or her letter board. Cut and attach a length of yarn to the top of the letter board for hanging. Hang completed Alphabet Mobiles from the ceiling or on a display board.

Letter Aa Pattern and Picture Squares

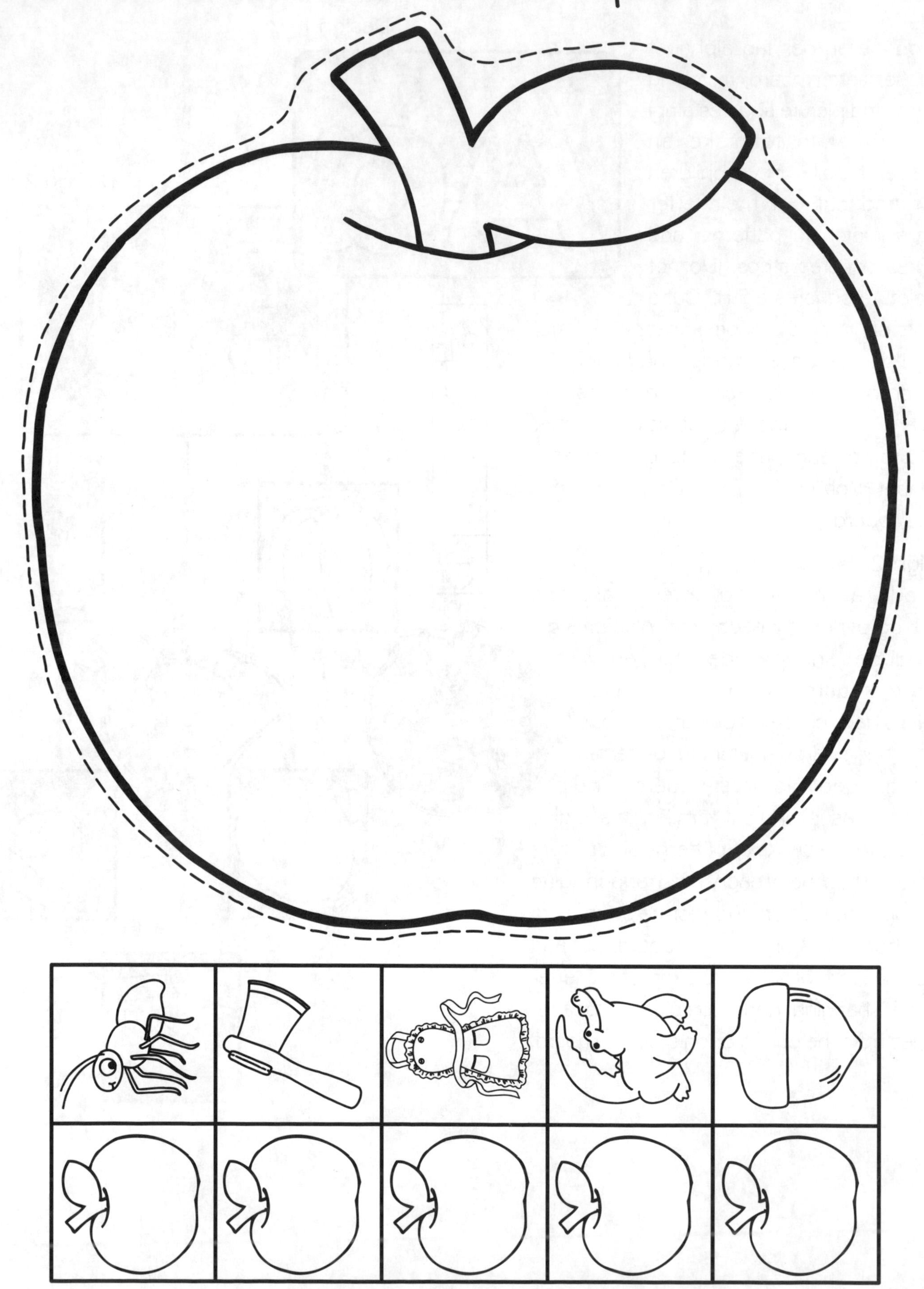

Letter Bb Pattern and Picture Squares

Letter Bb Board

Letter Cc Pattern and Picture Squares

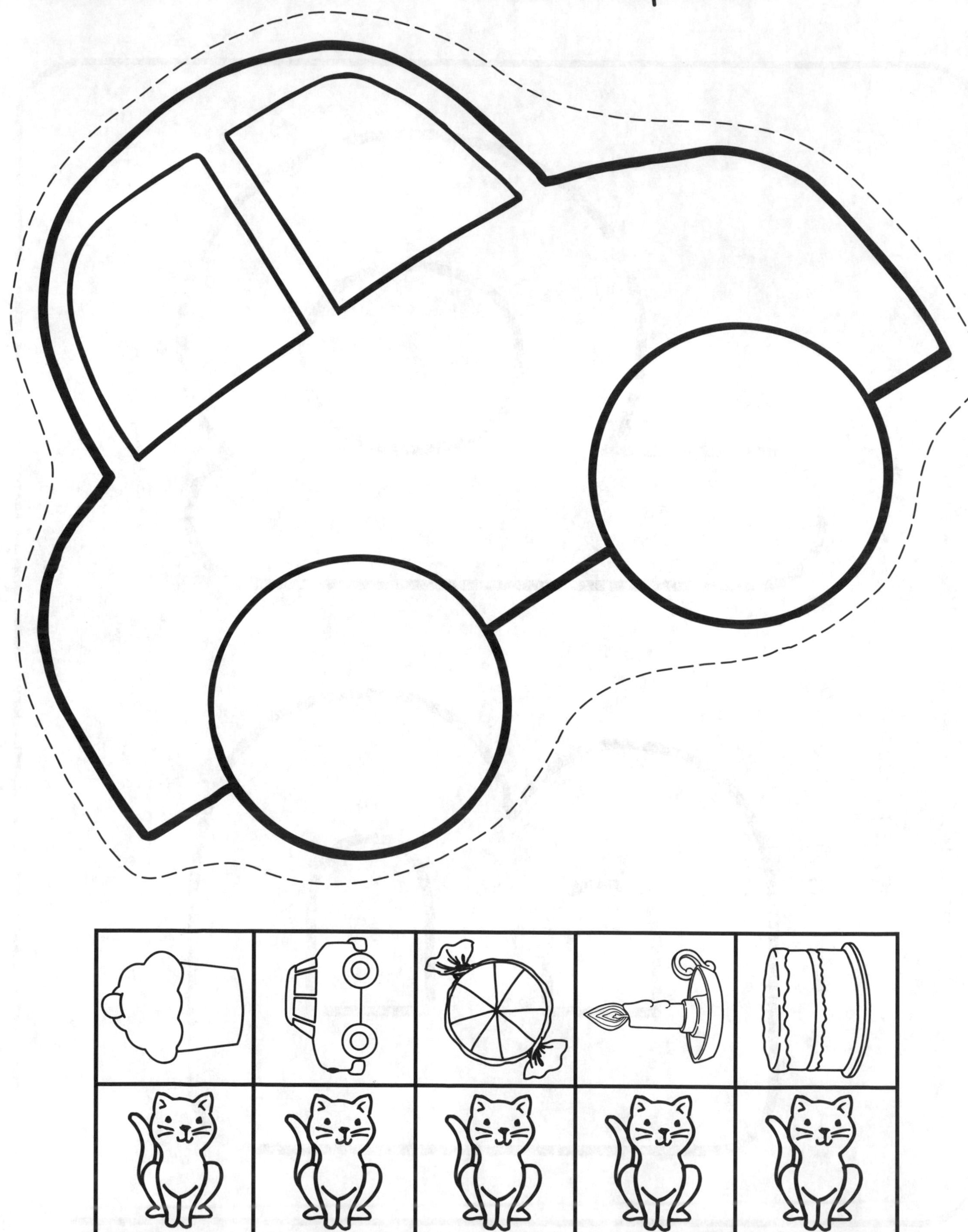

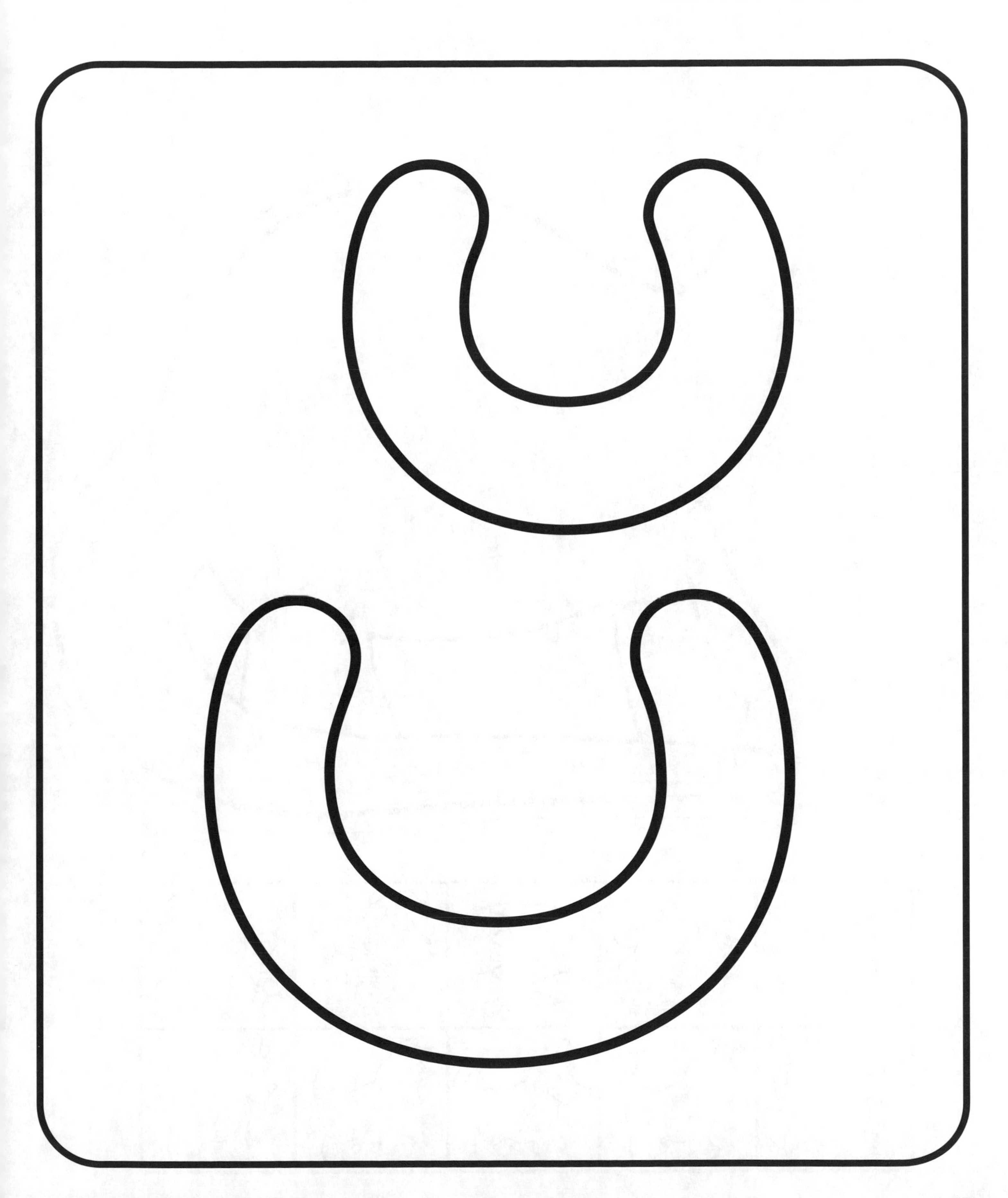

Letter Dd Pattern and Picture Squares

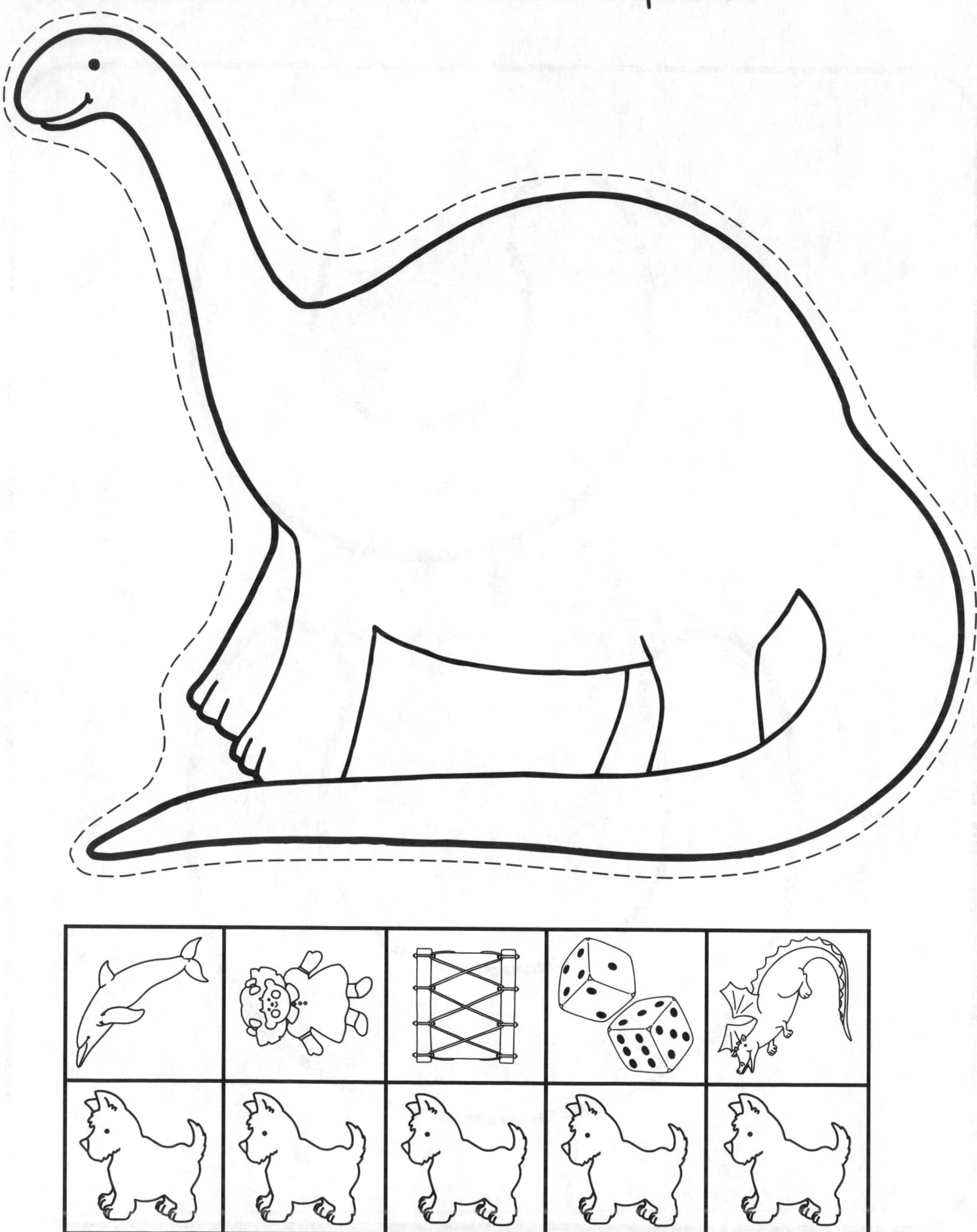

Letter Dd Board

Letter Ee Pattern and Picture Squares

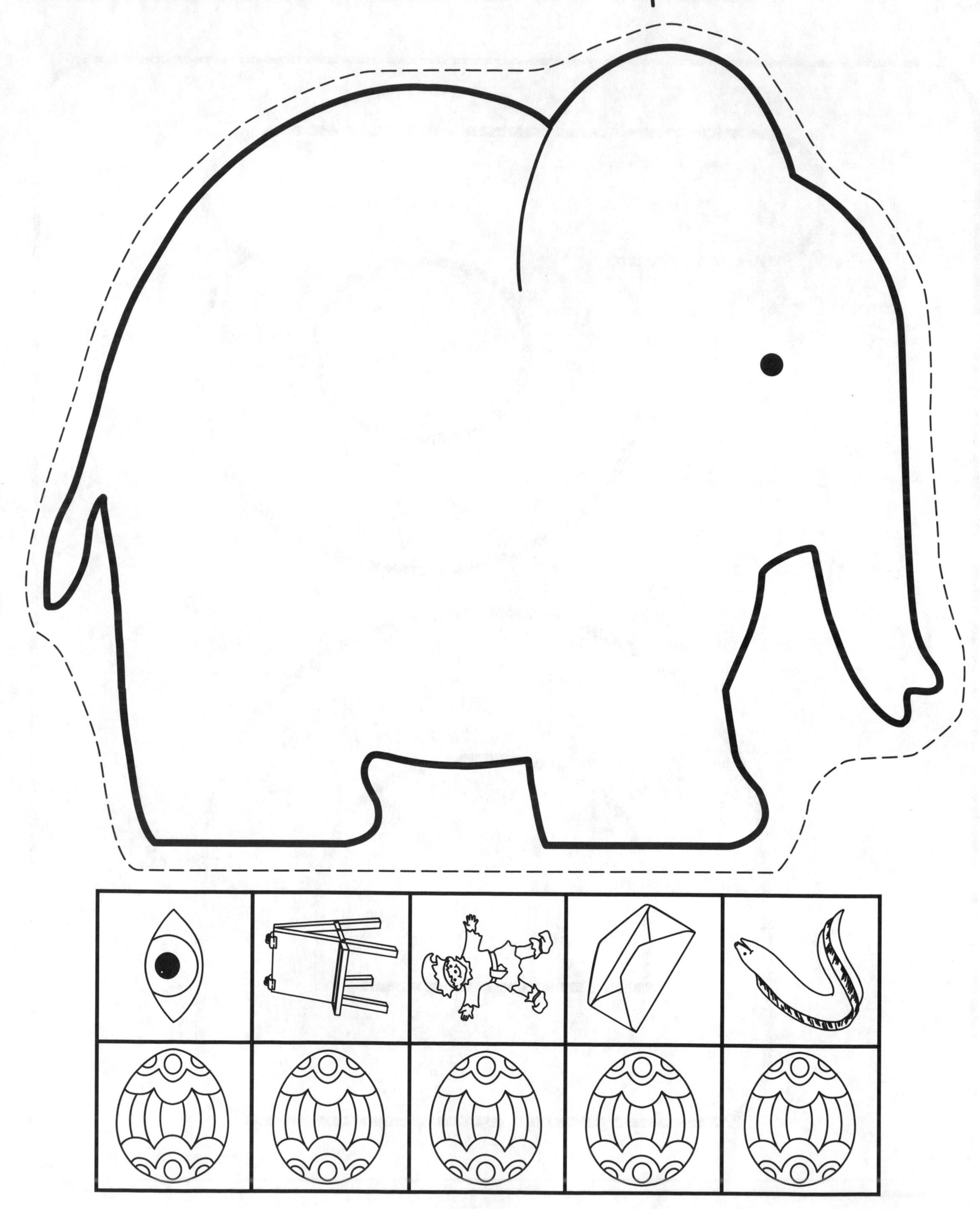

Letter Ee Board

Letter Ff Pattern and Picture Squares

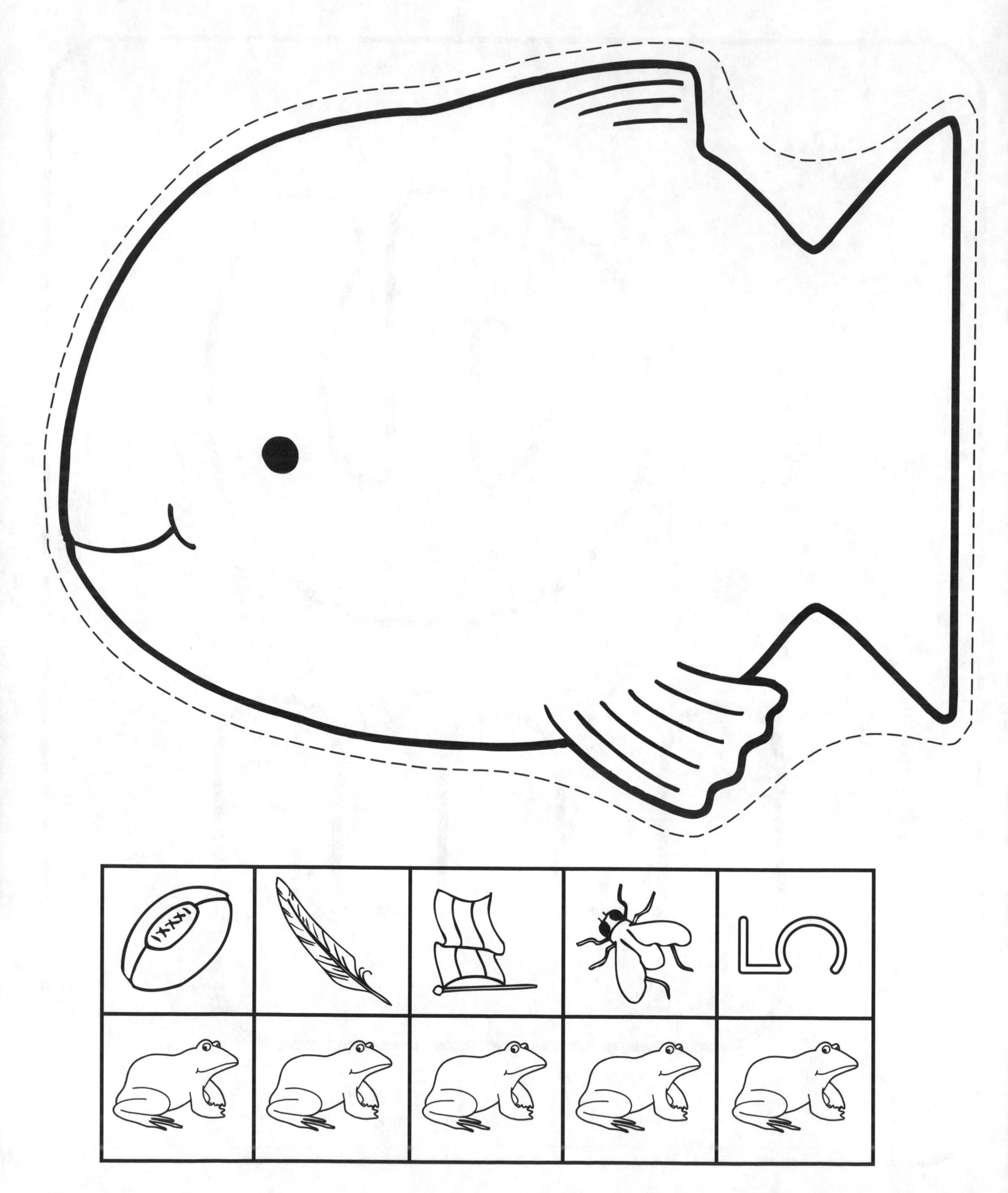

Letter Ff Board

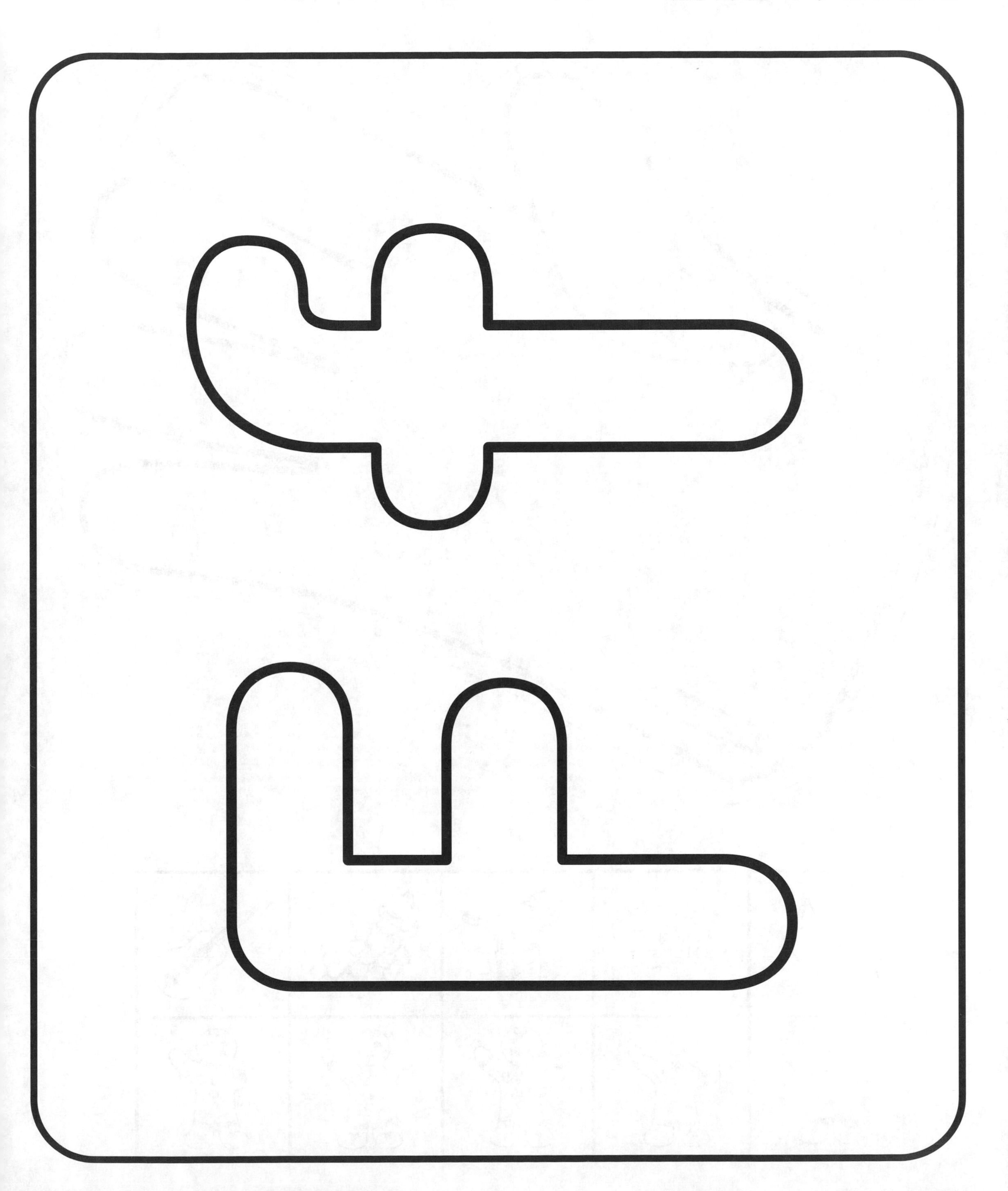

Letter Gg Pattern and Picture Squares

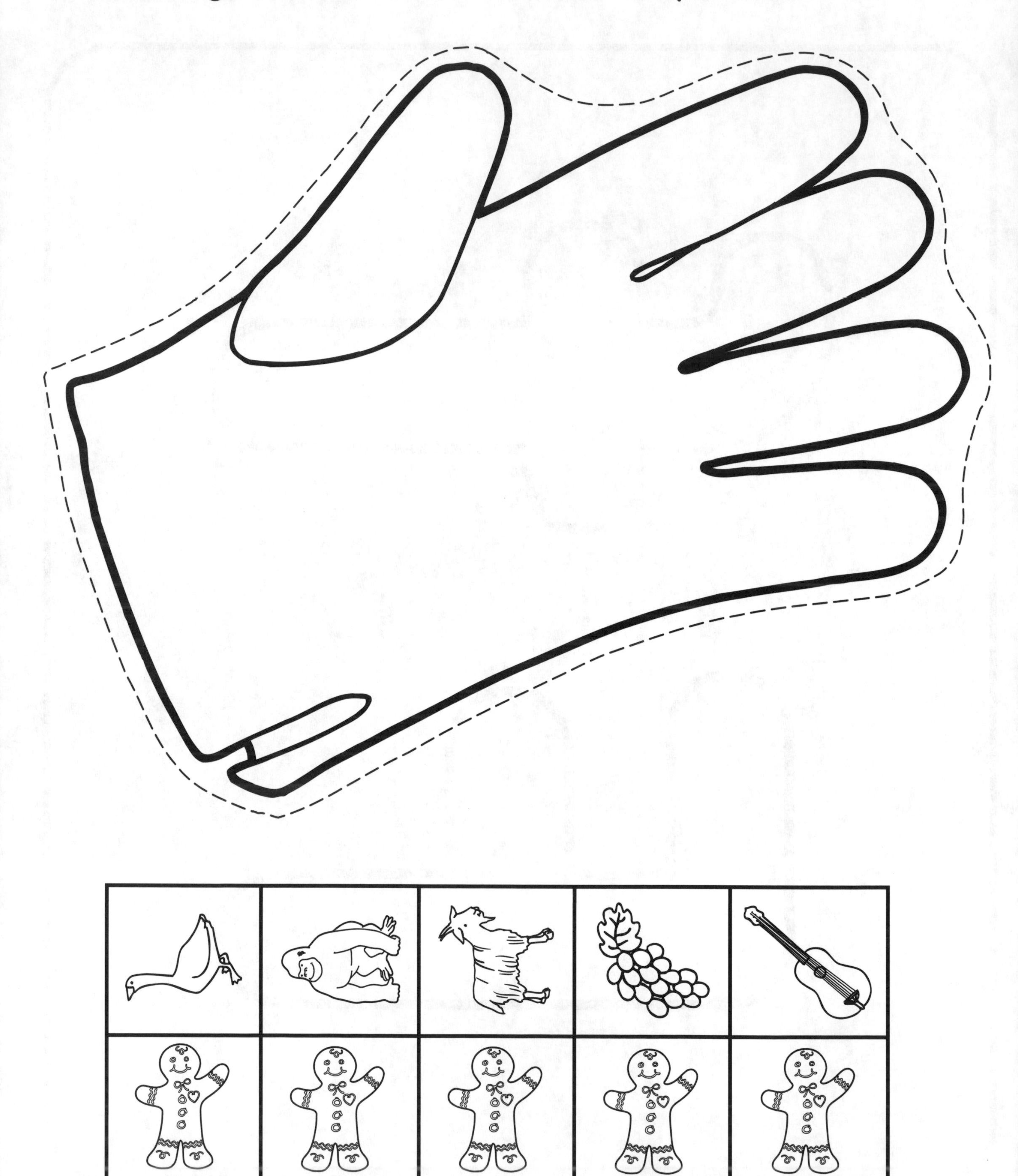

Letter Gg Board

Letter Hh Pattern and Picture Squares

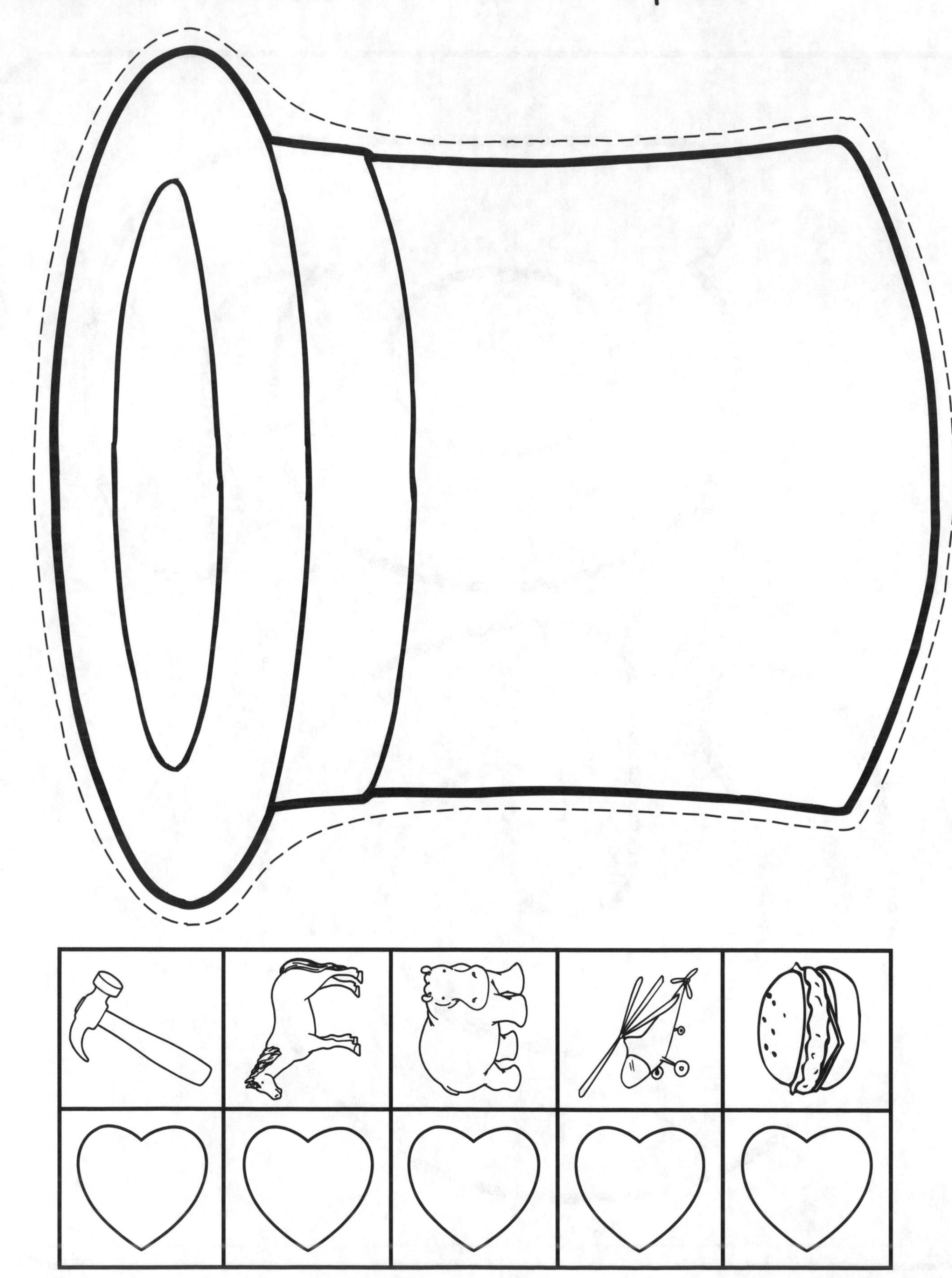

Letter Hh Board

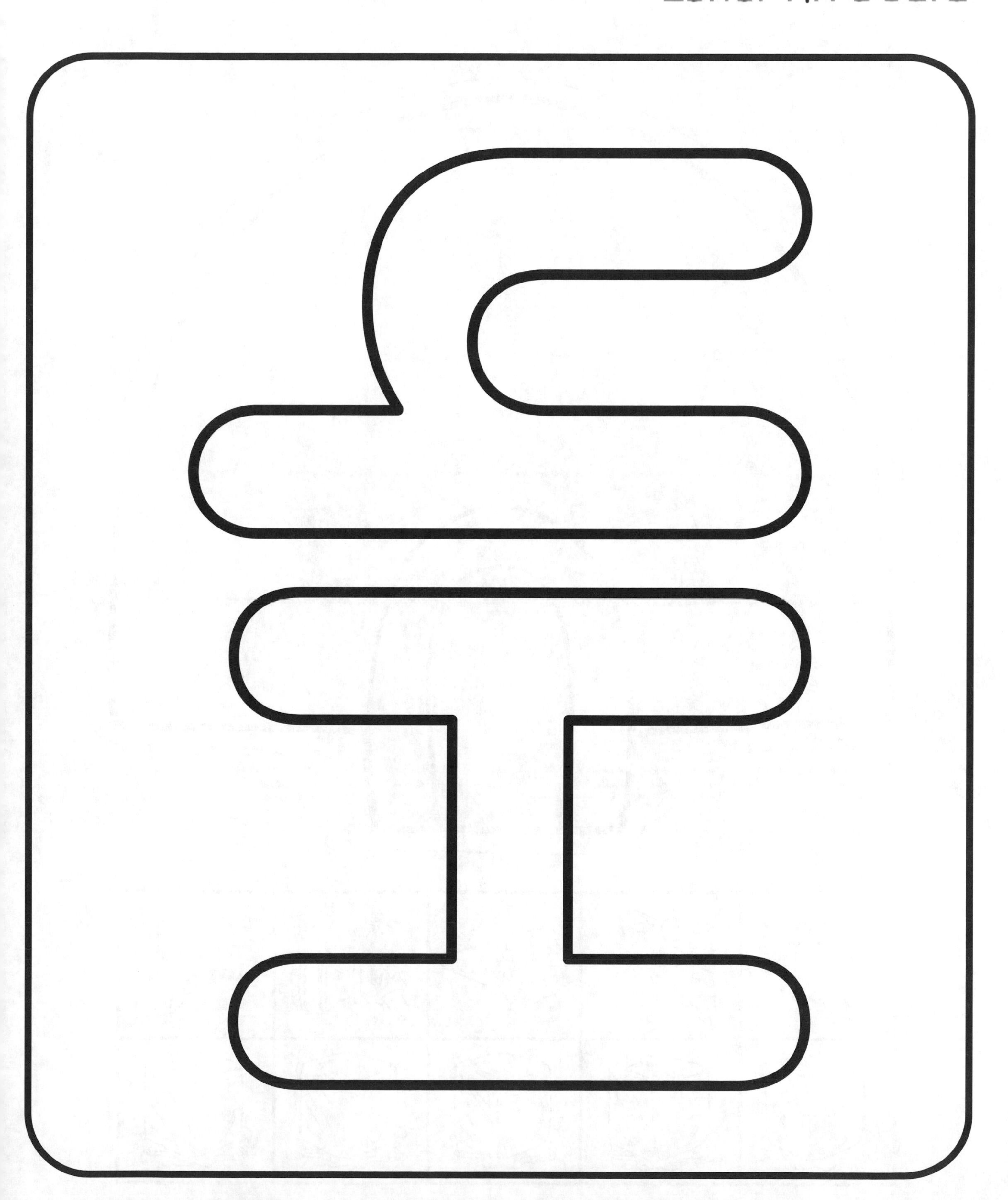

Letter Ii Pattern and Picture Squares

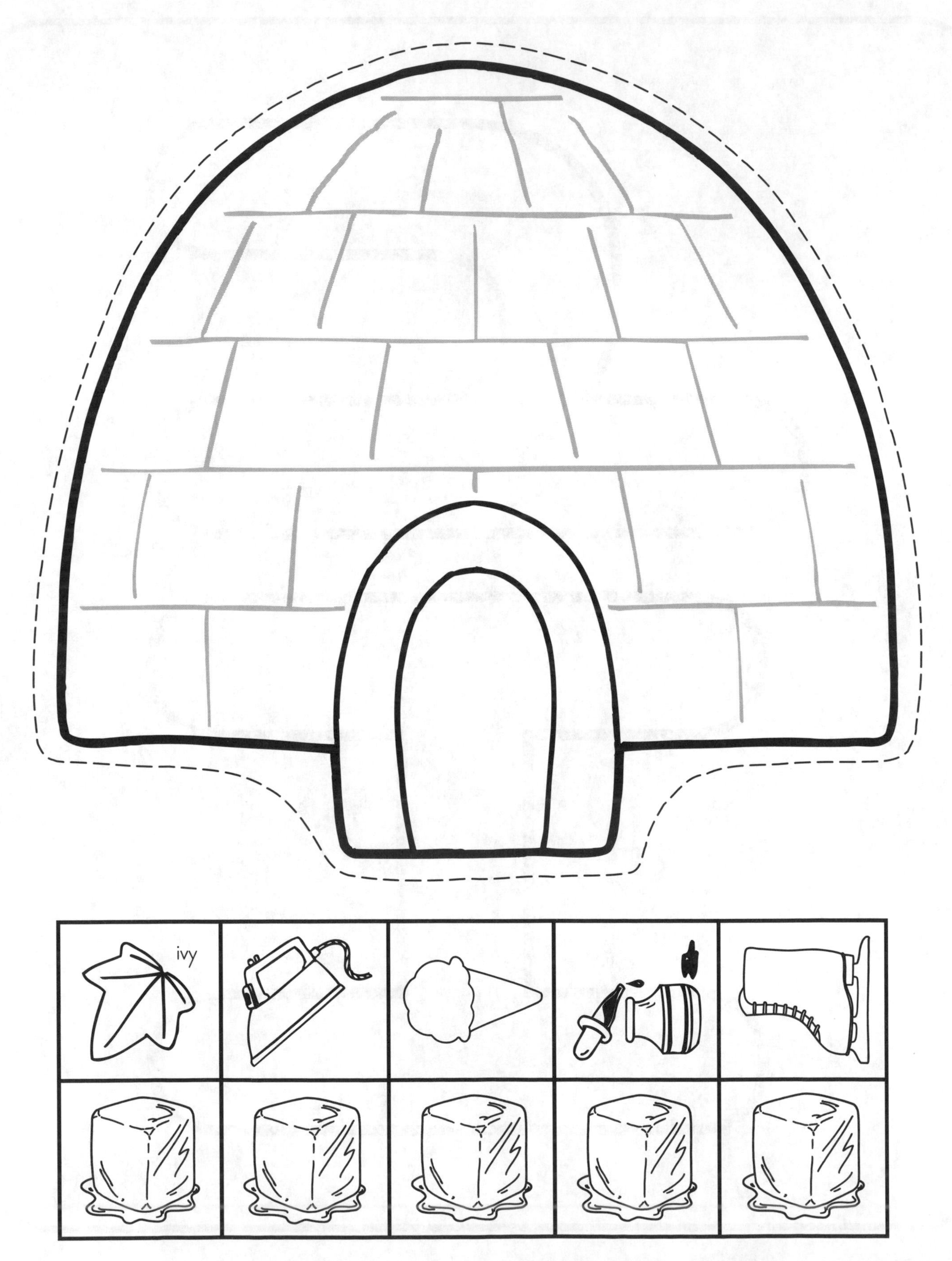

Letter Ii Board

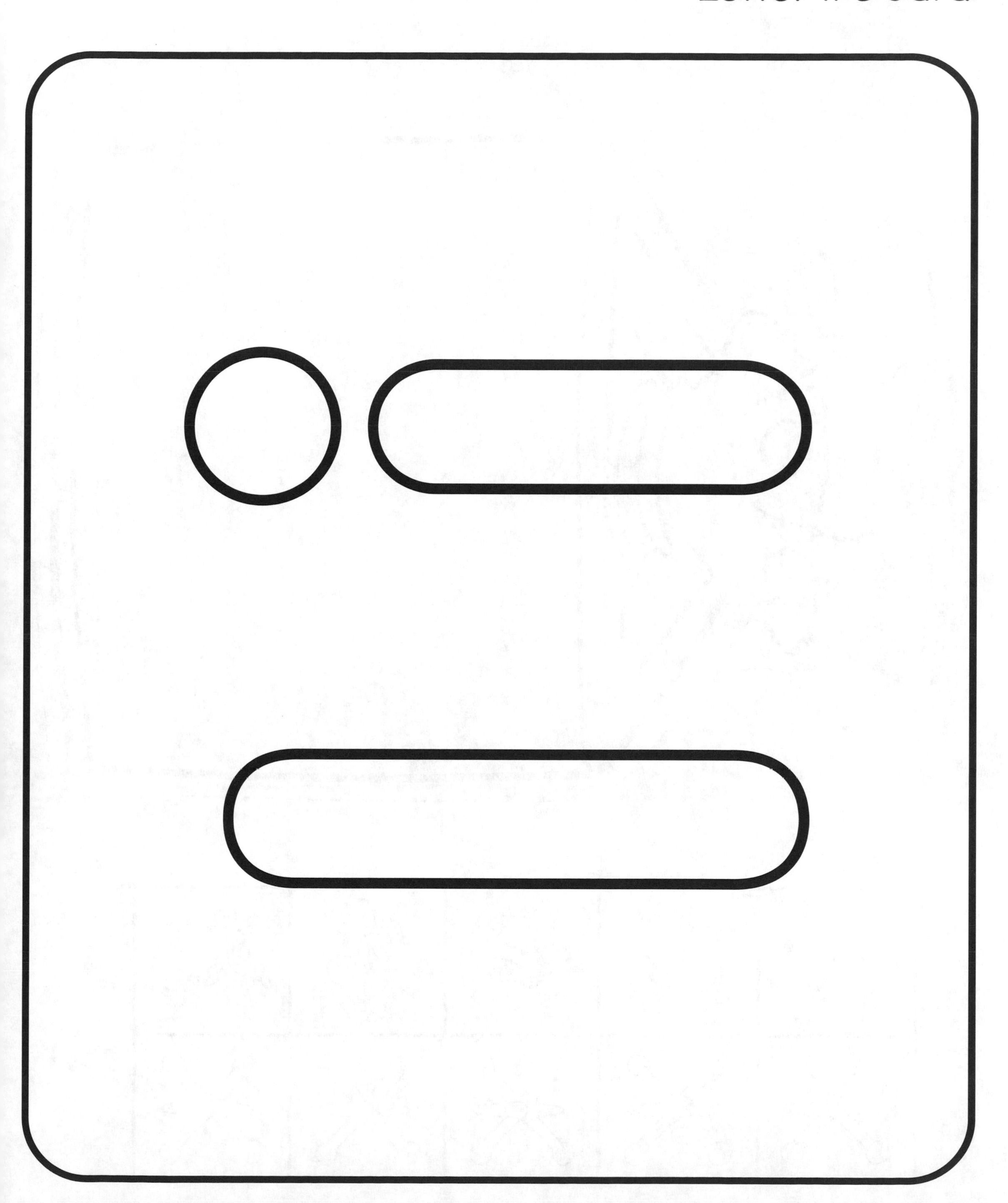

Letter Jj Pattern and Picture Squares

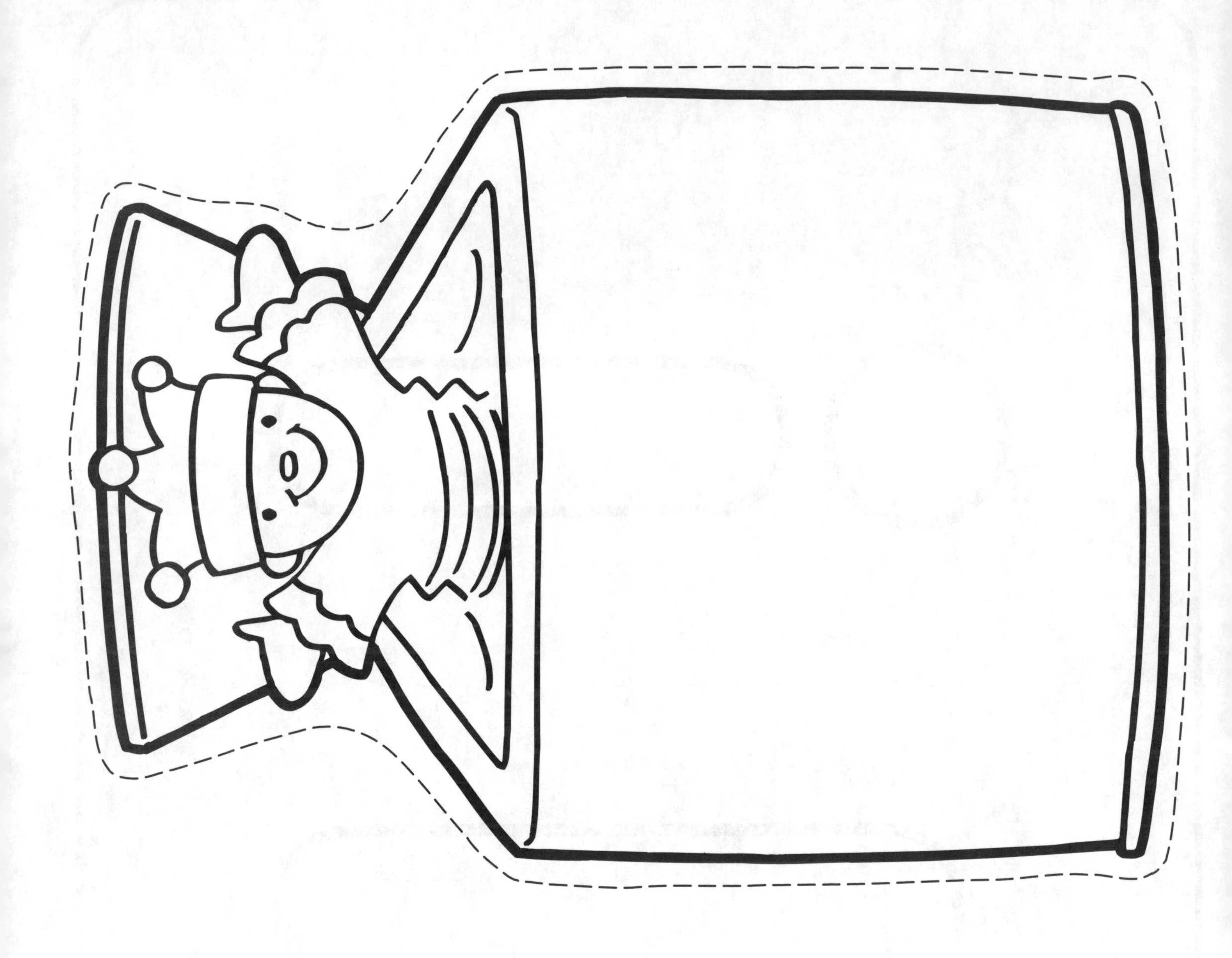

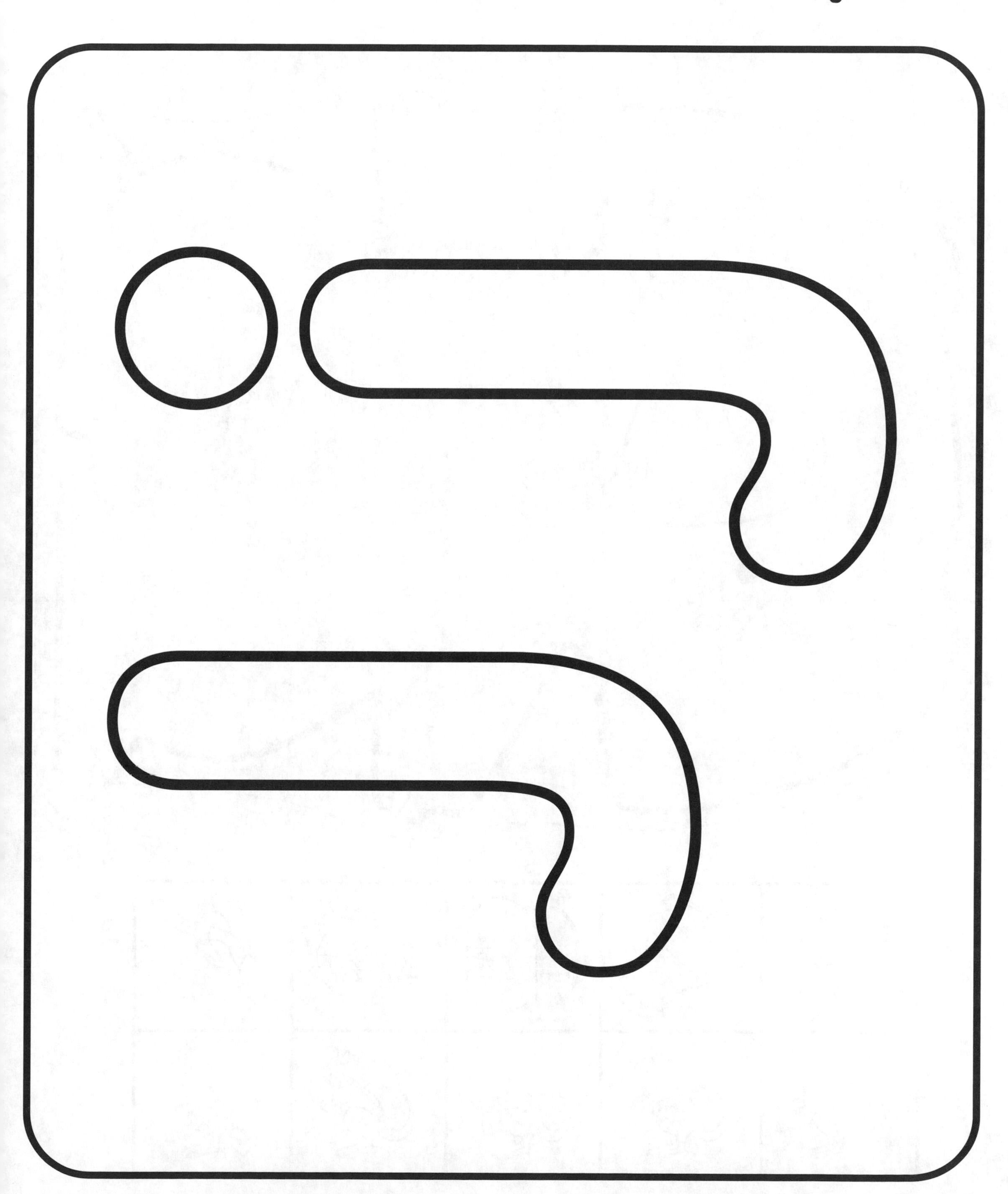

Letter Kk Pattern and Picture Squares

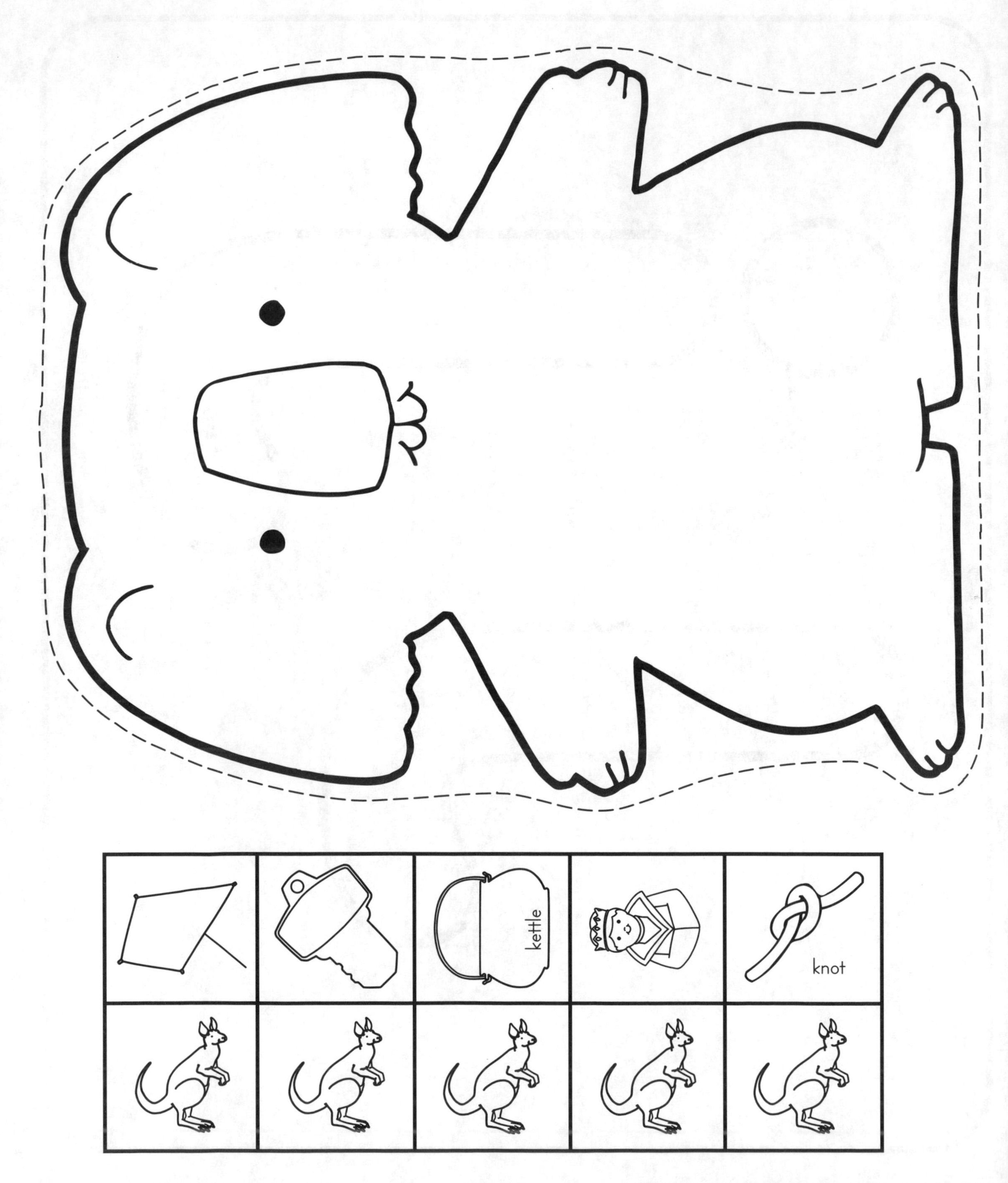

Letter Kk Board

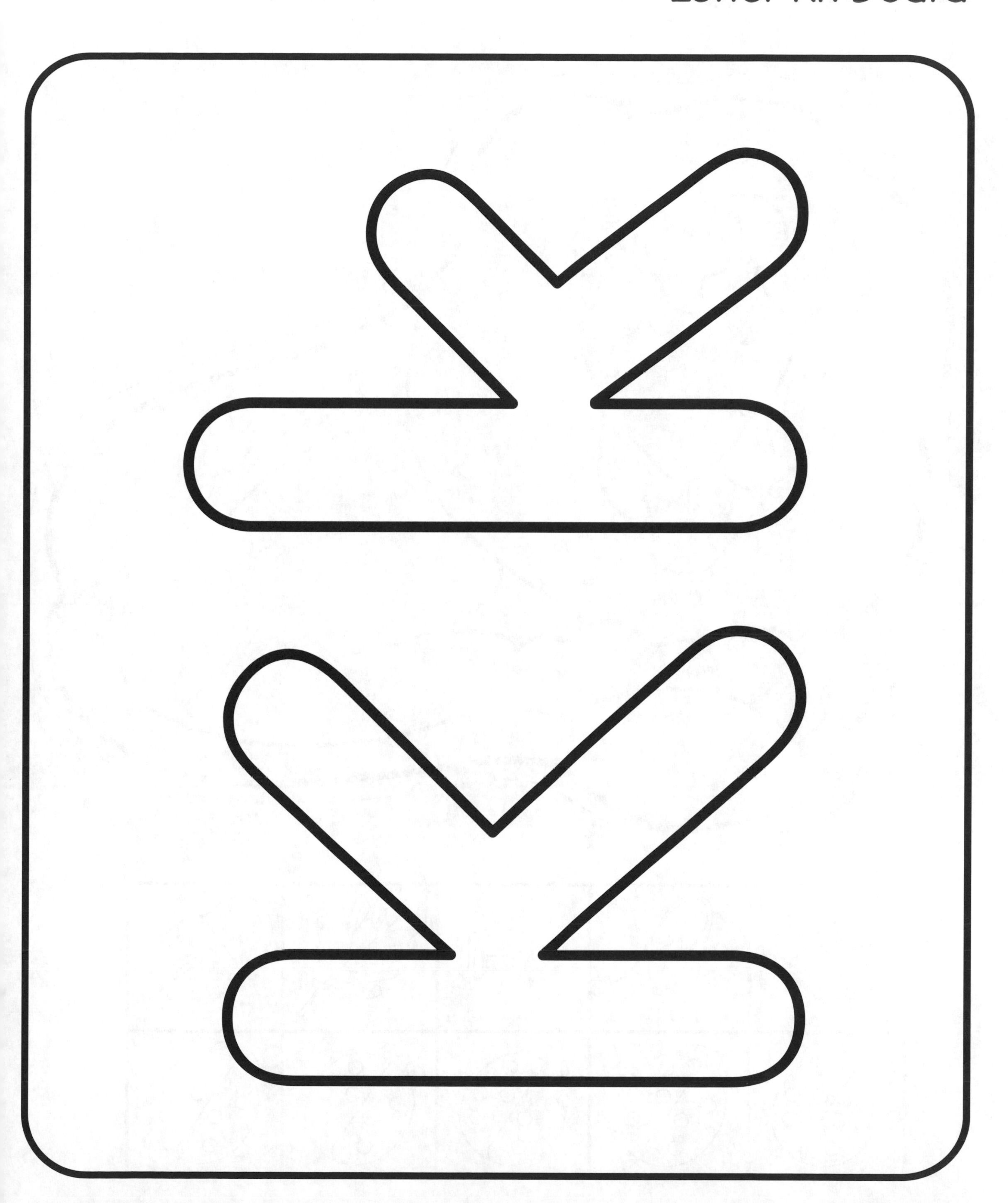

Letter Ll Pattern and Picture Squares

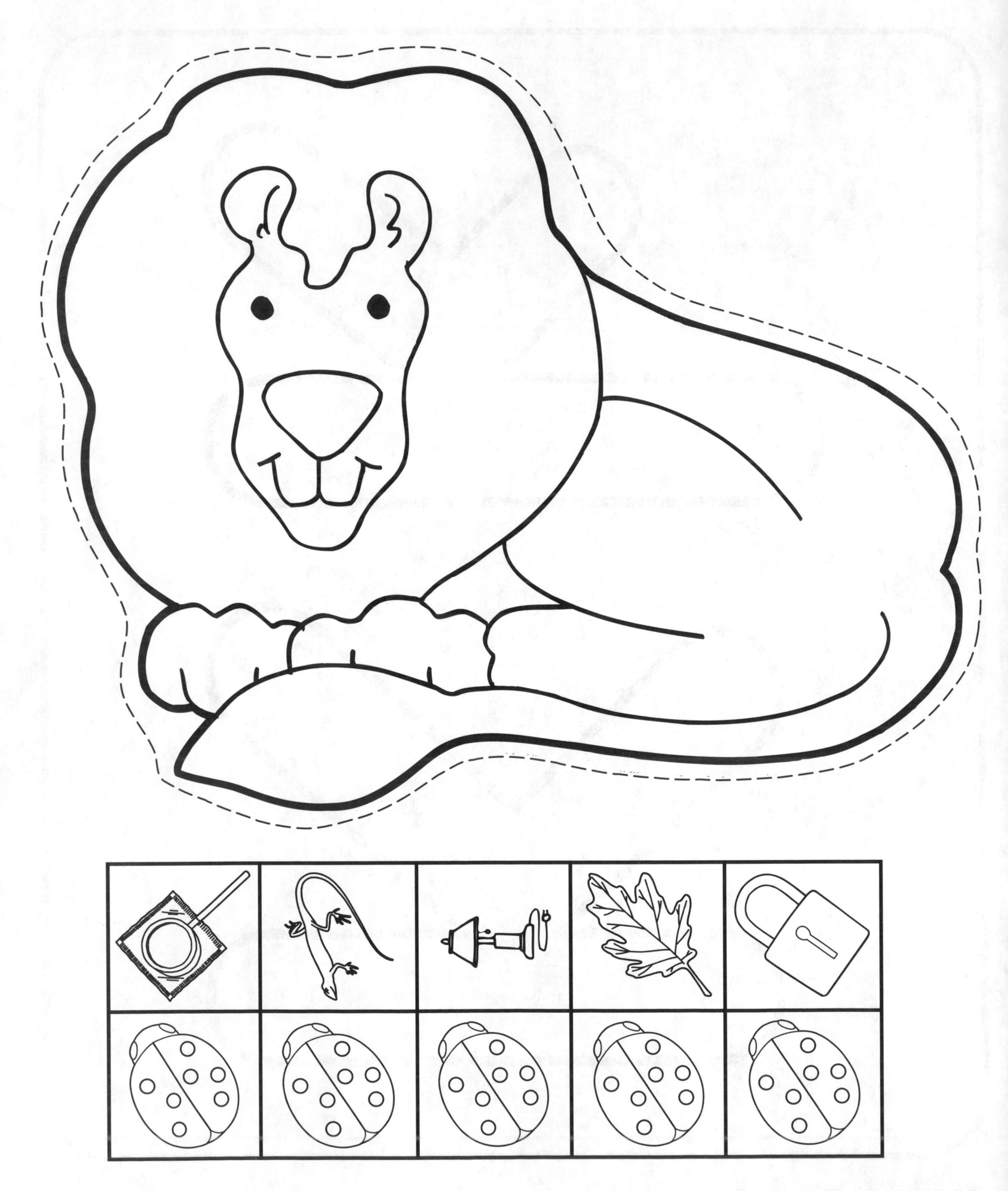

Letter Ll Board

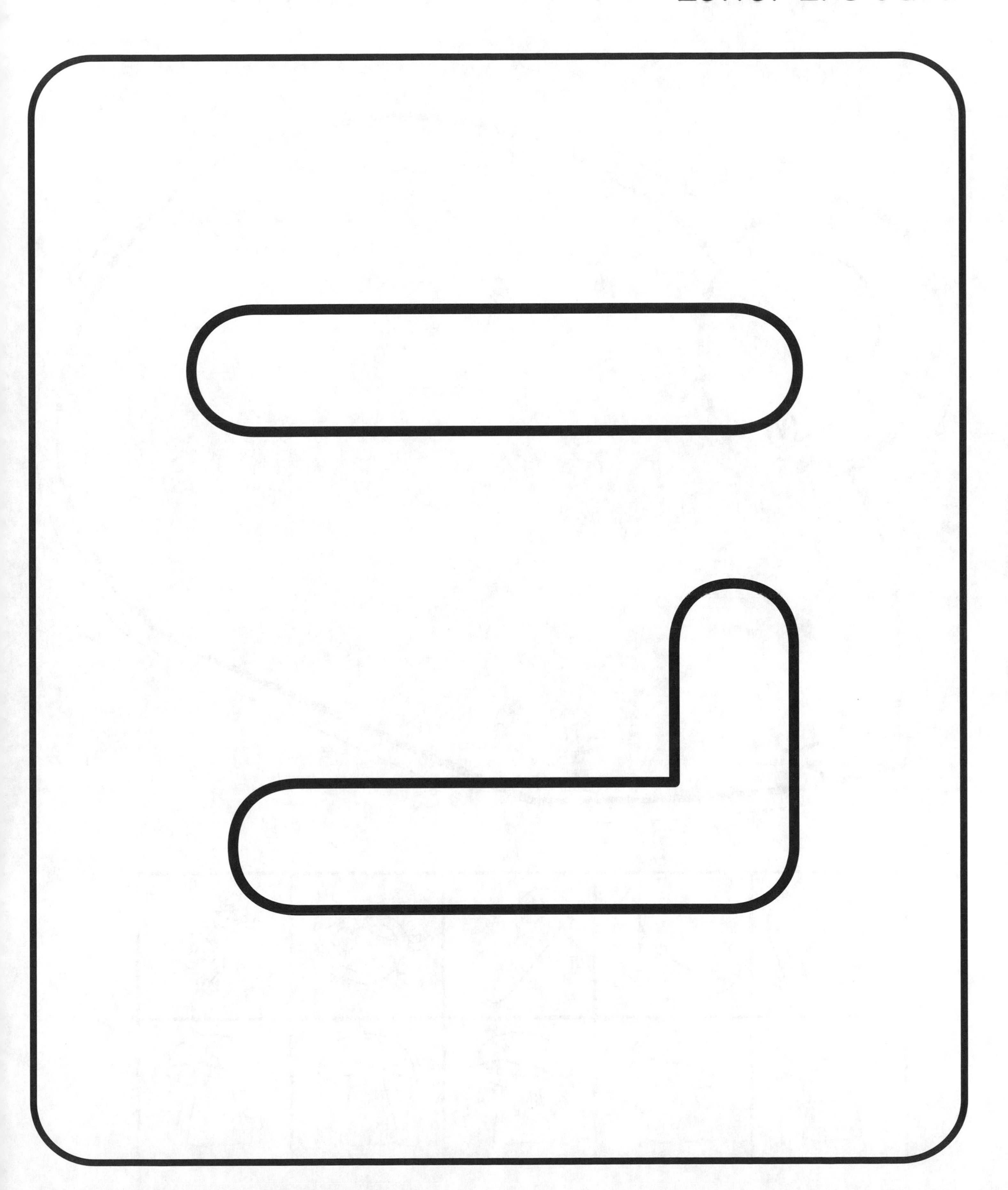

Letter Mm Pattern and Picture Squares

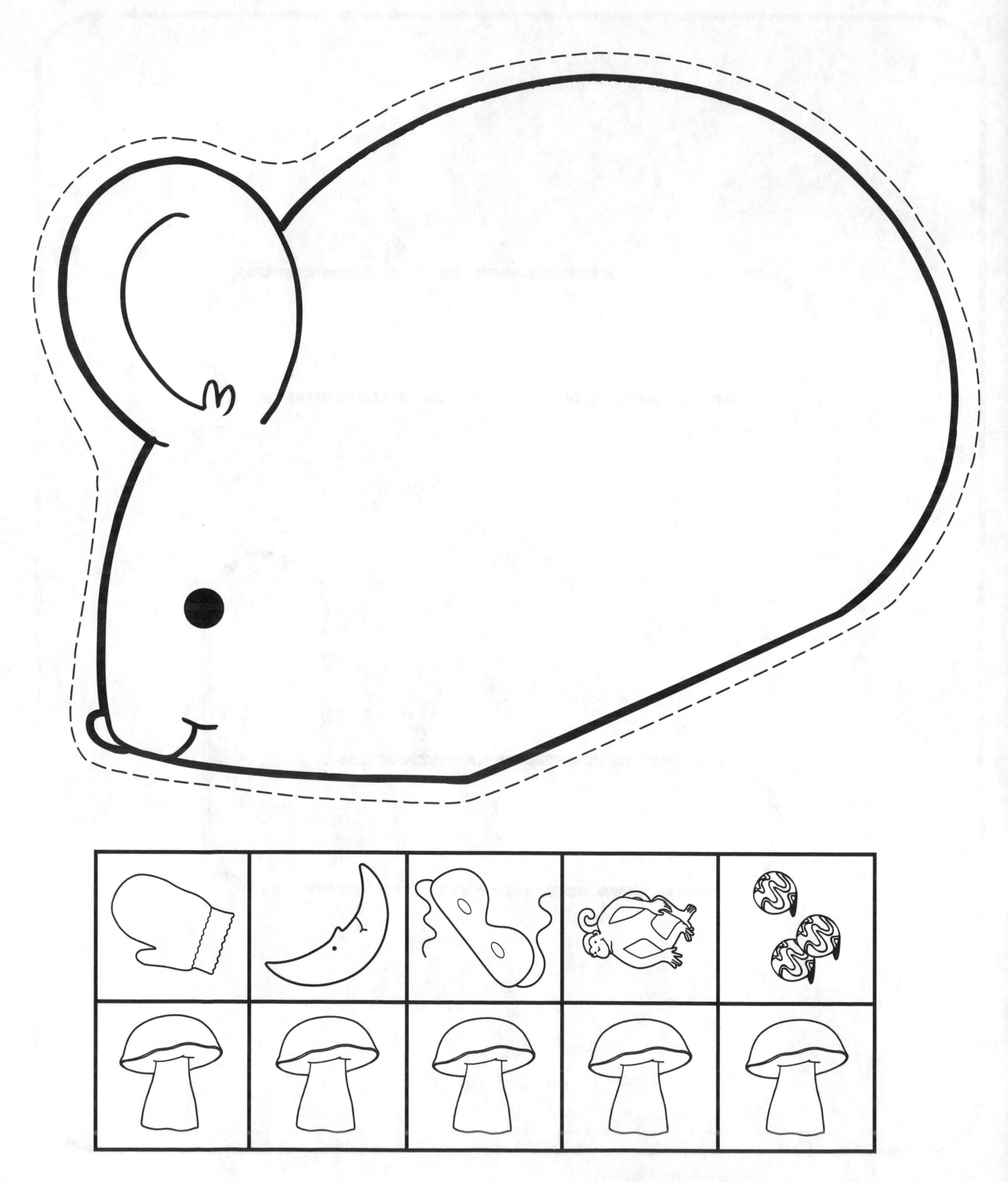

Letter Mm Board

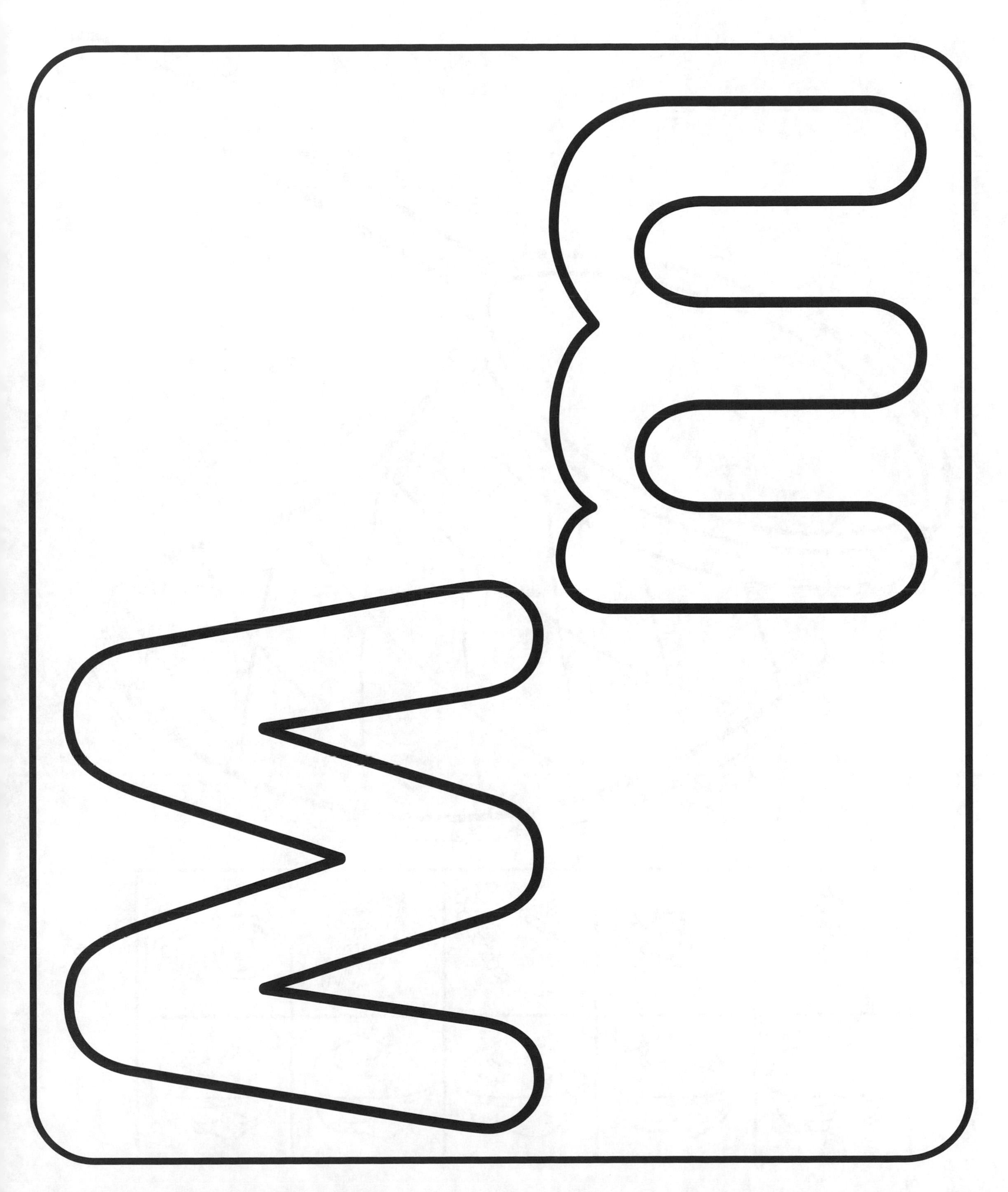

Letter Nn Pattern and Picture Squares

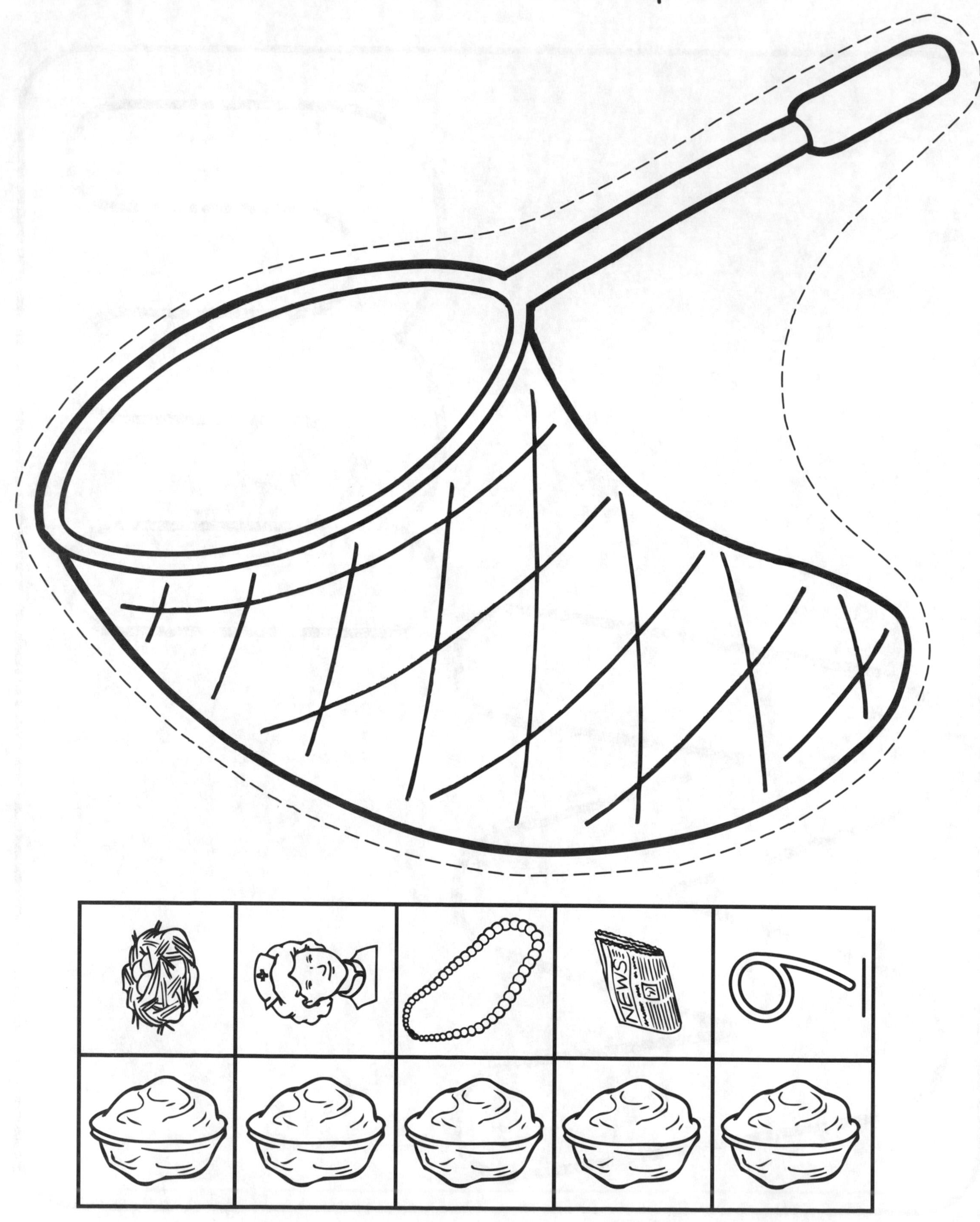

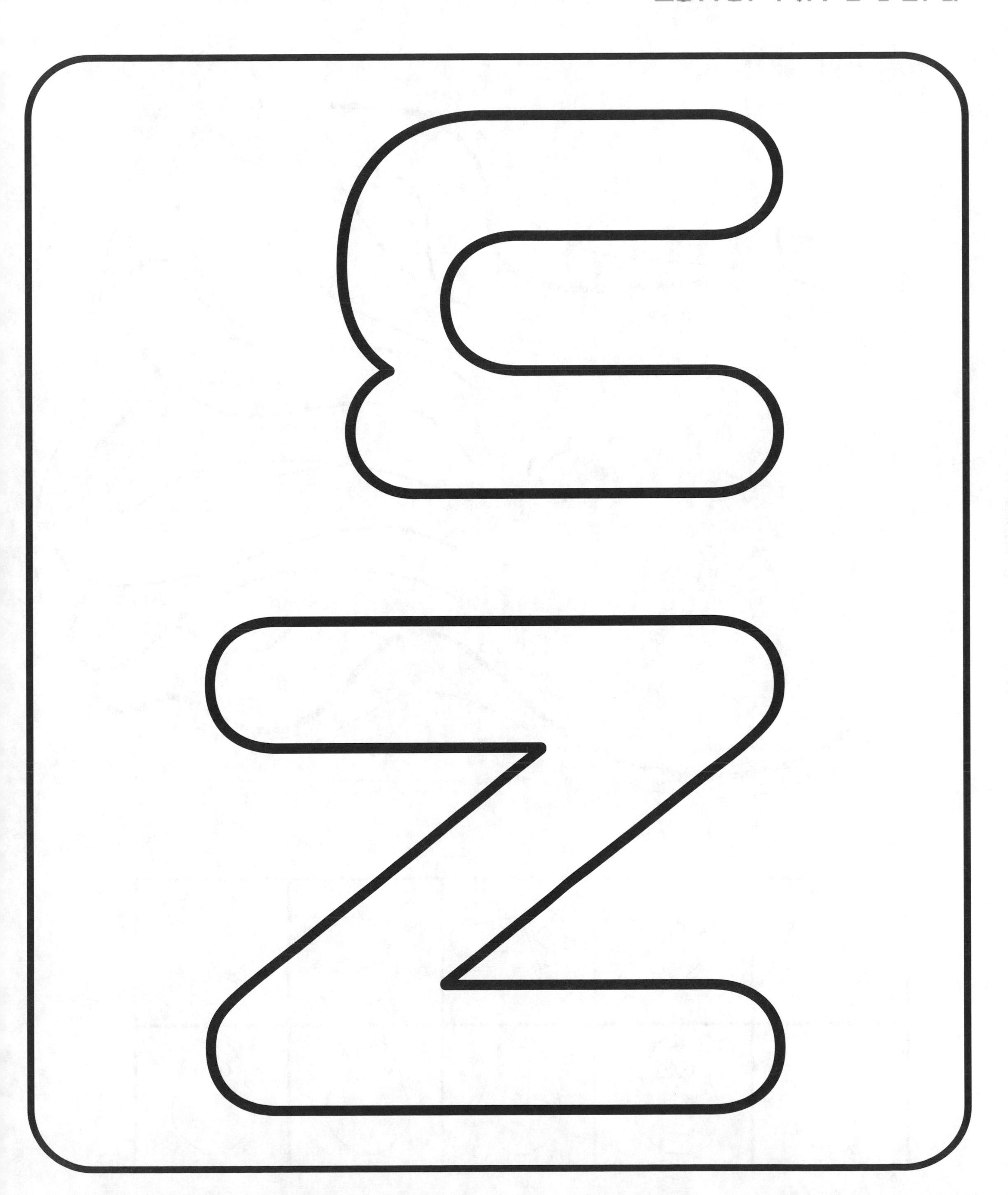

Letter Oo Pattern and Picture Squares

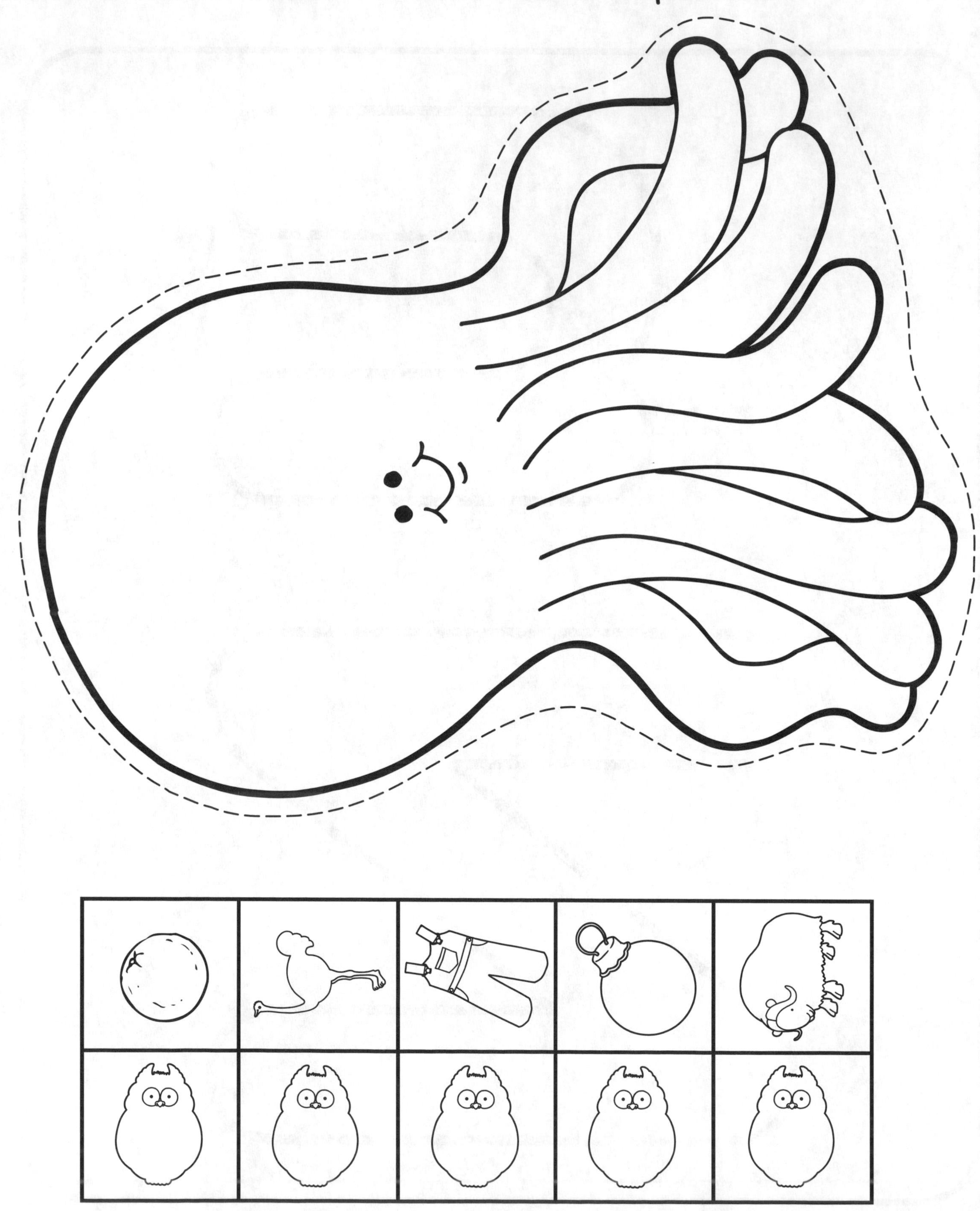

Letter Pp Pattern and Picture Squares

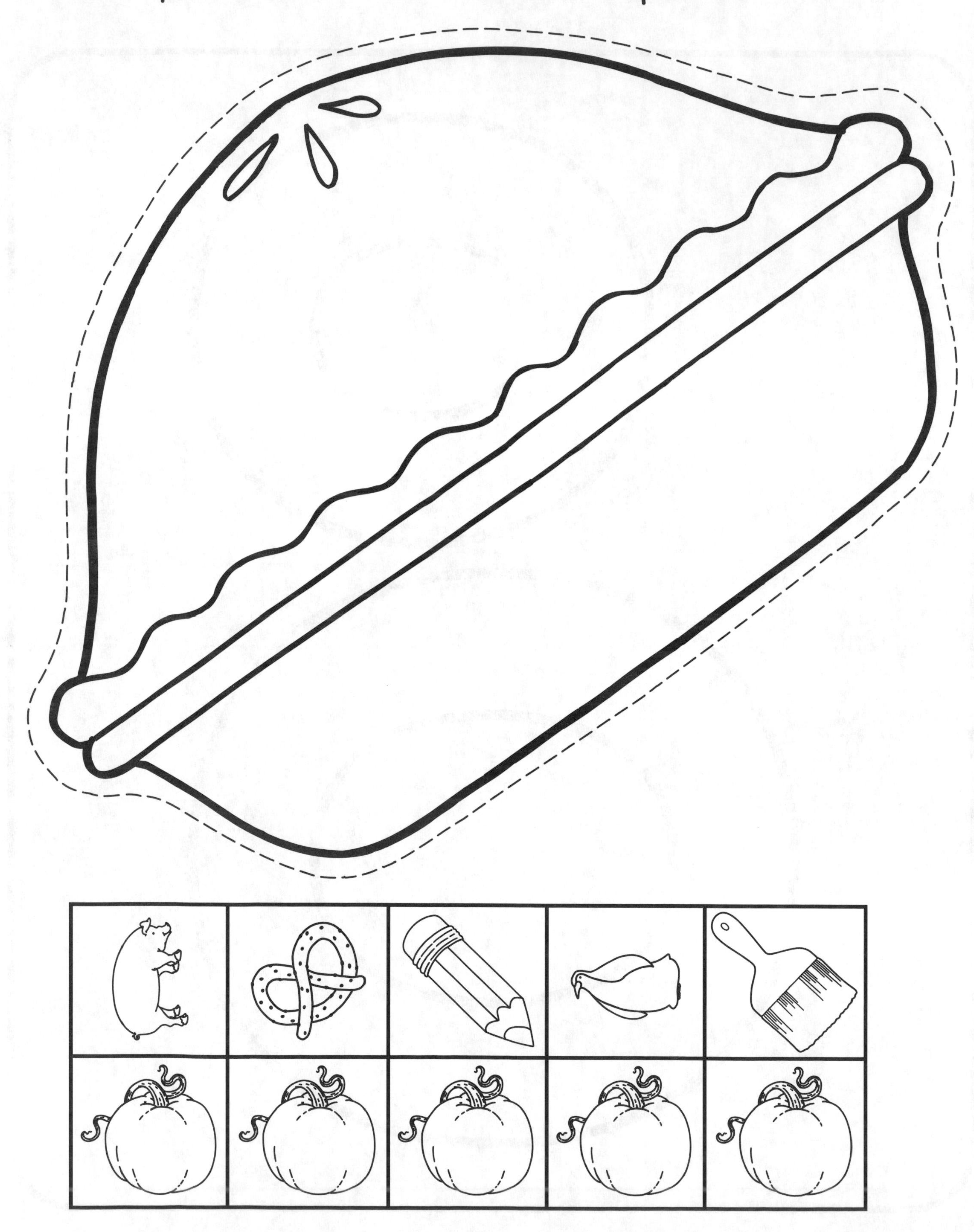

Letter Pp Board

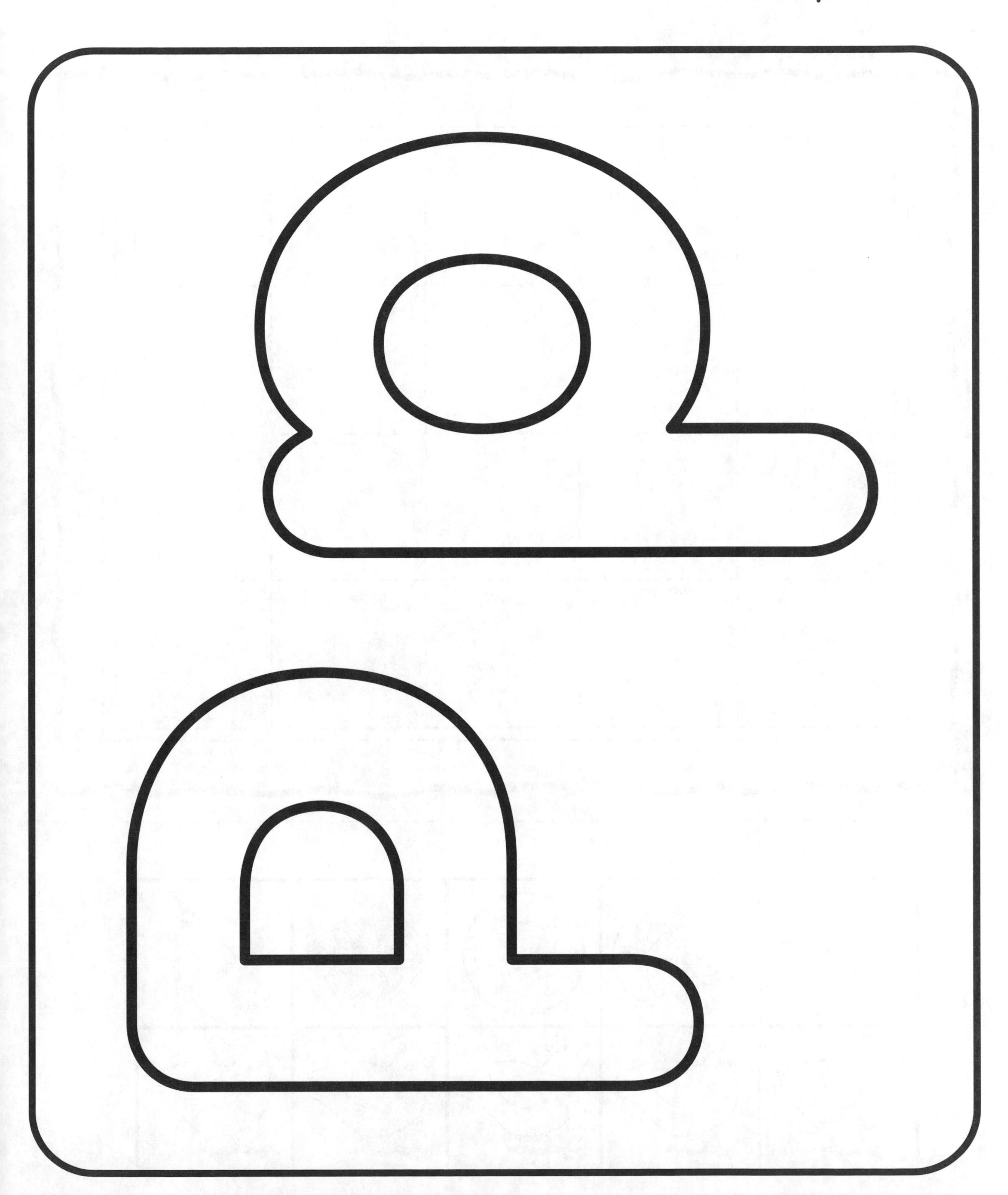

Letter Qq Pattern and Picture Squares

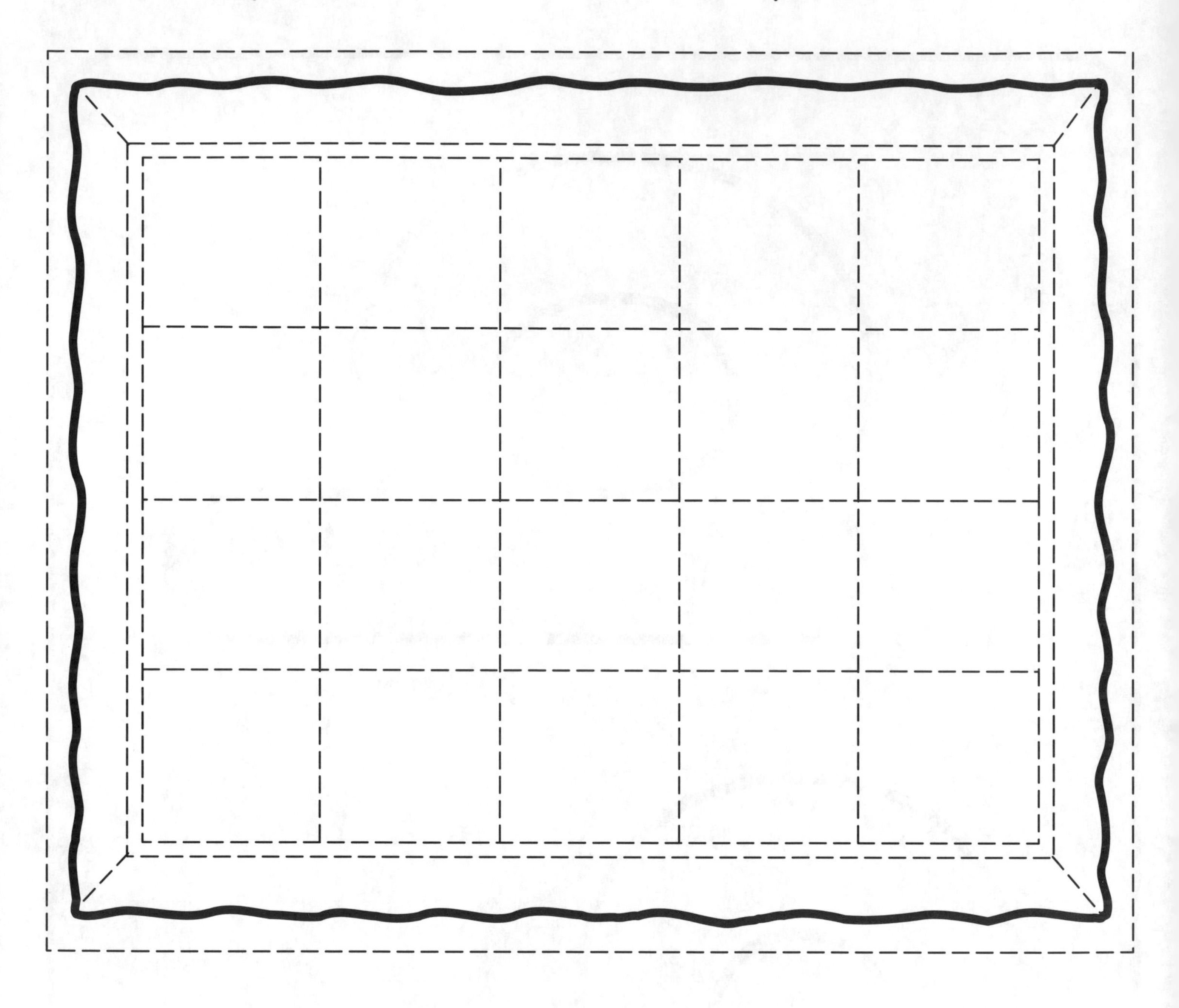

Letter Rr Pattern and Picture Squares

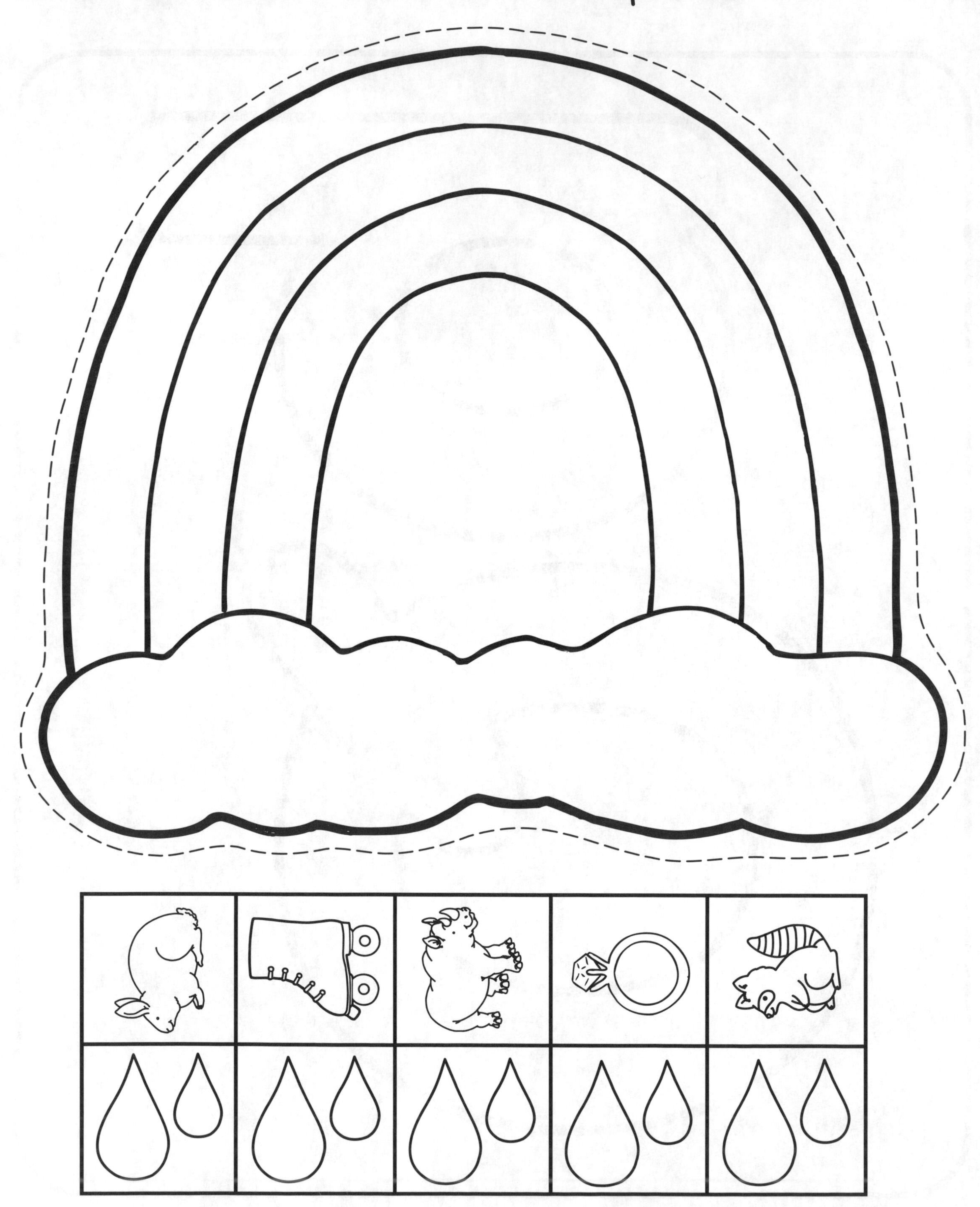

Letter Rr Board

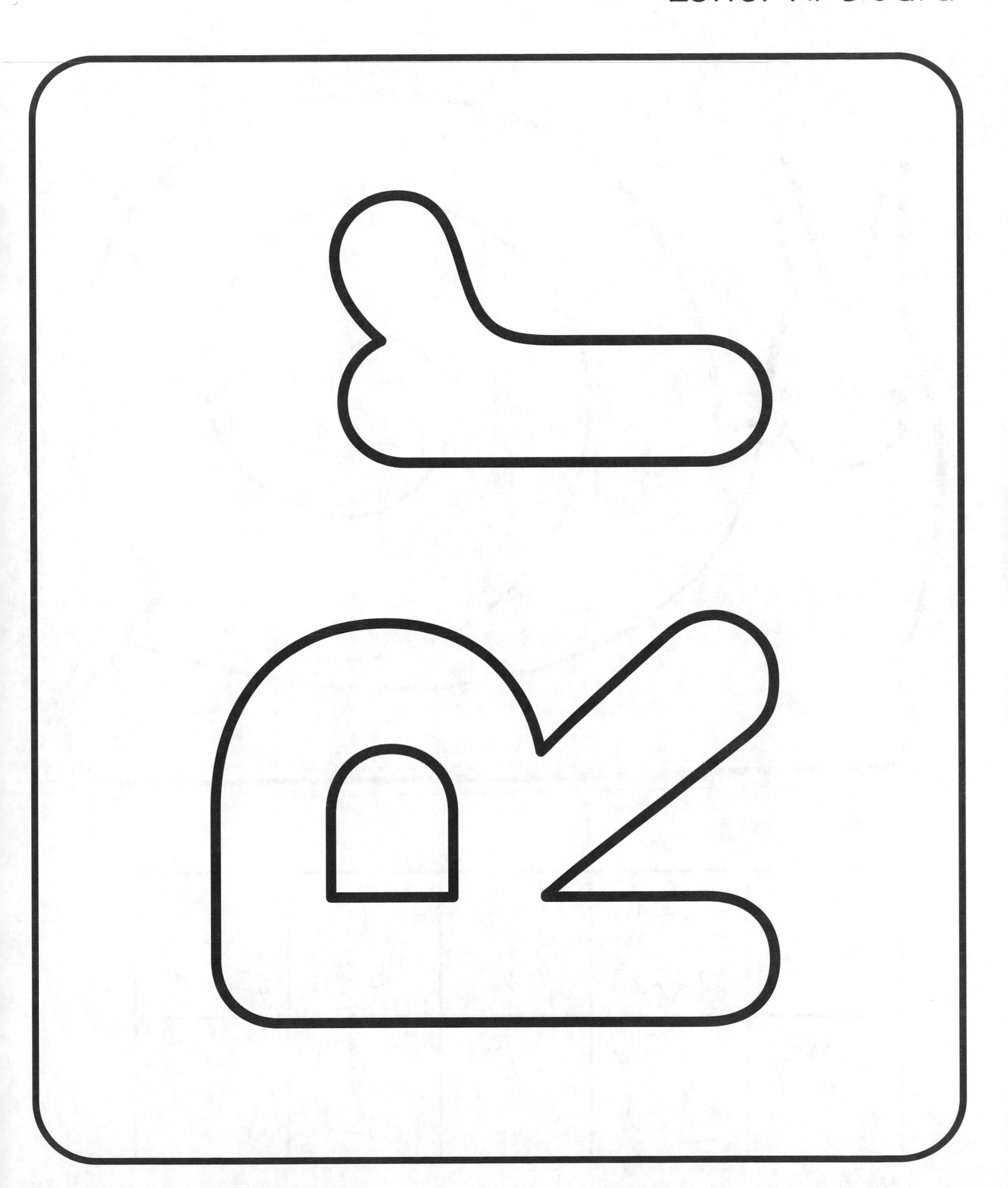

Letter Ss Pattern and Picture Squares

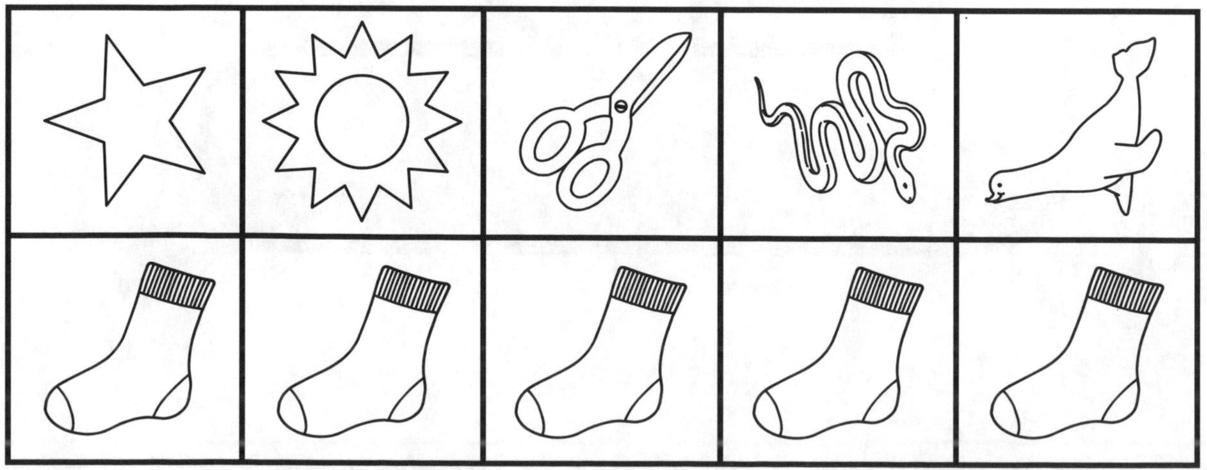

Letter Tt Pattern and Picture Squares

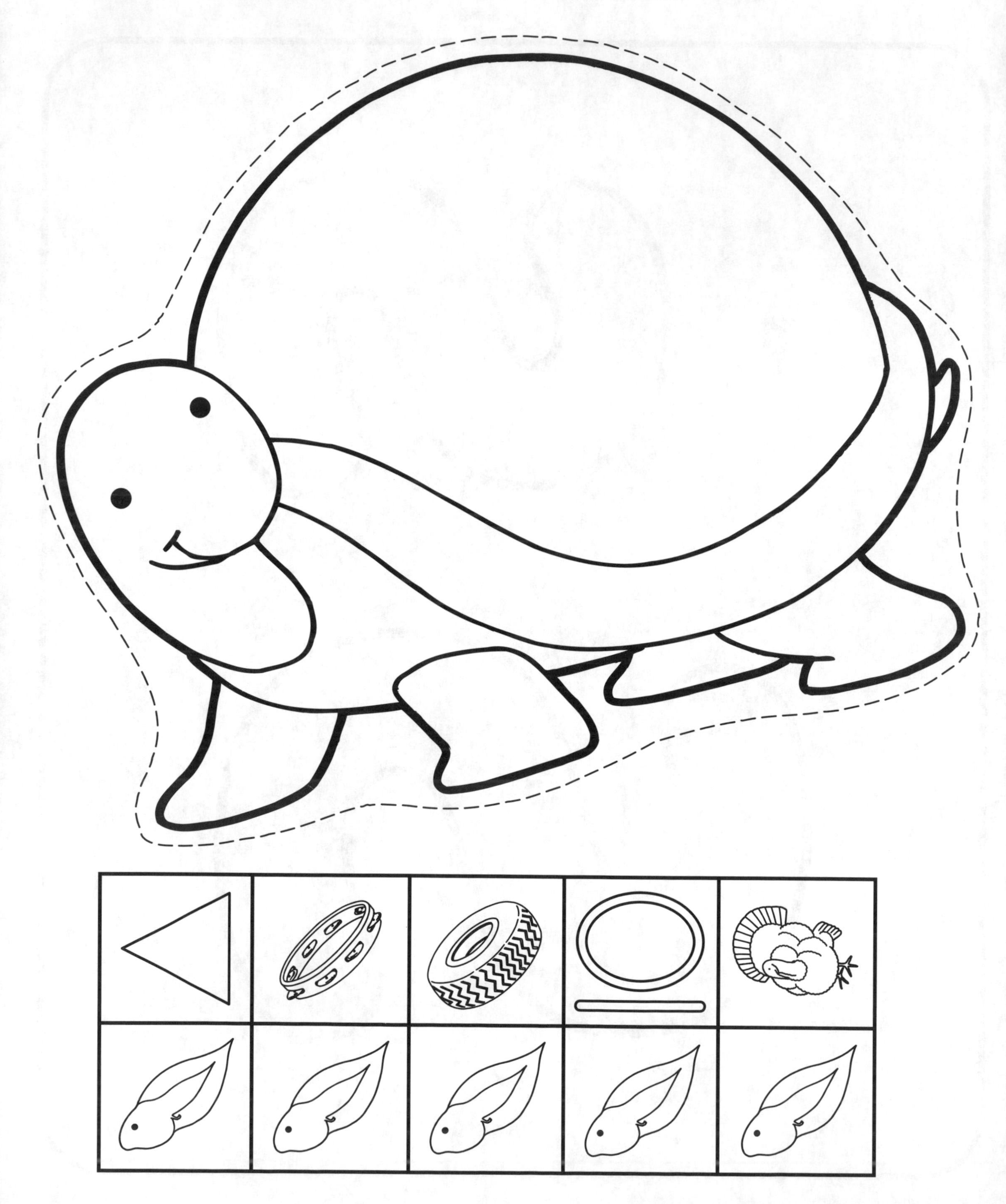

Letter Tt Board

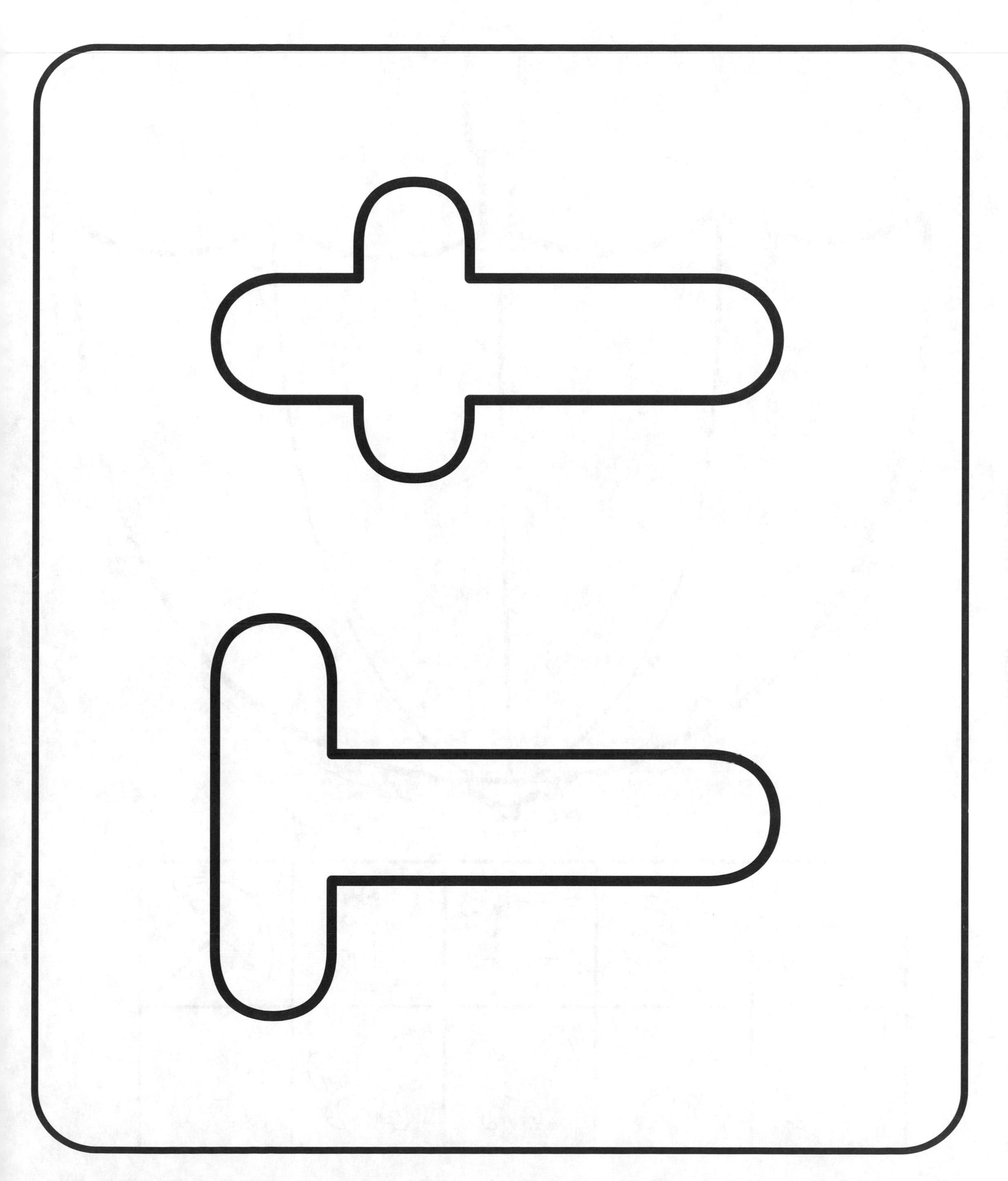

Letter Uu Pattern and Picture Squares

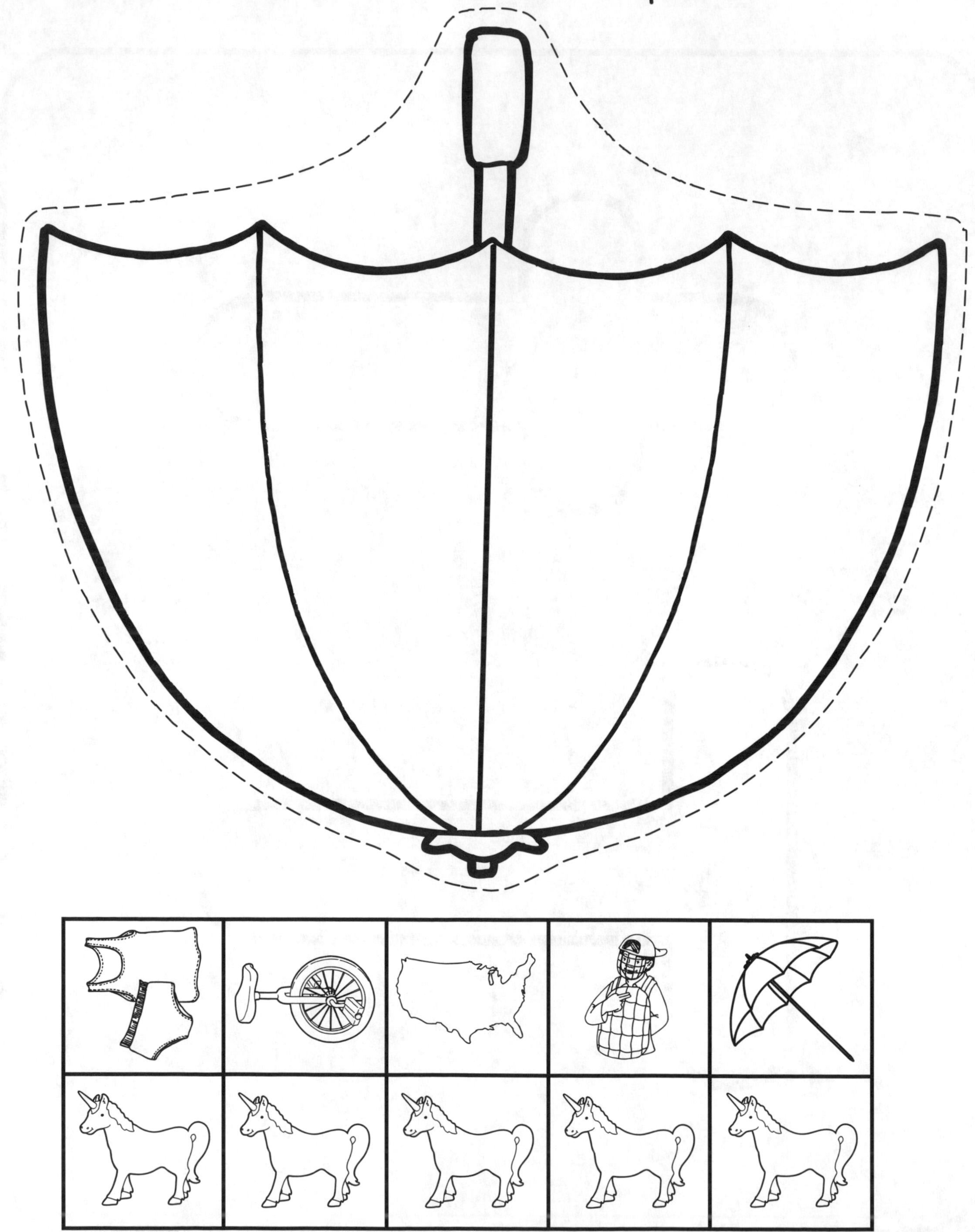

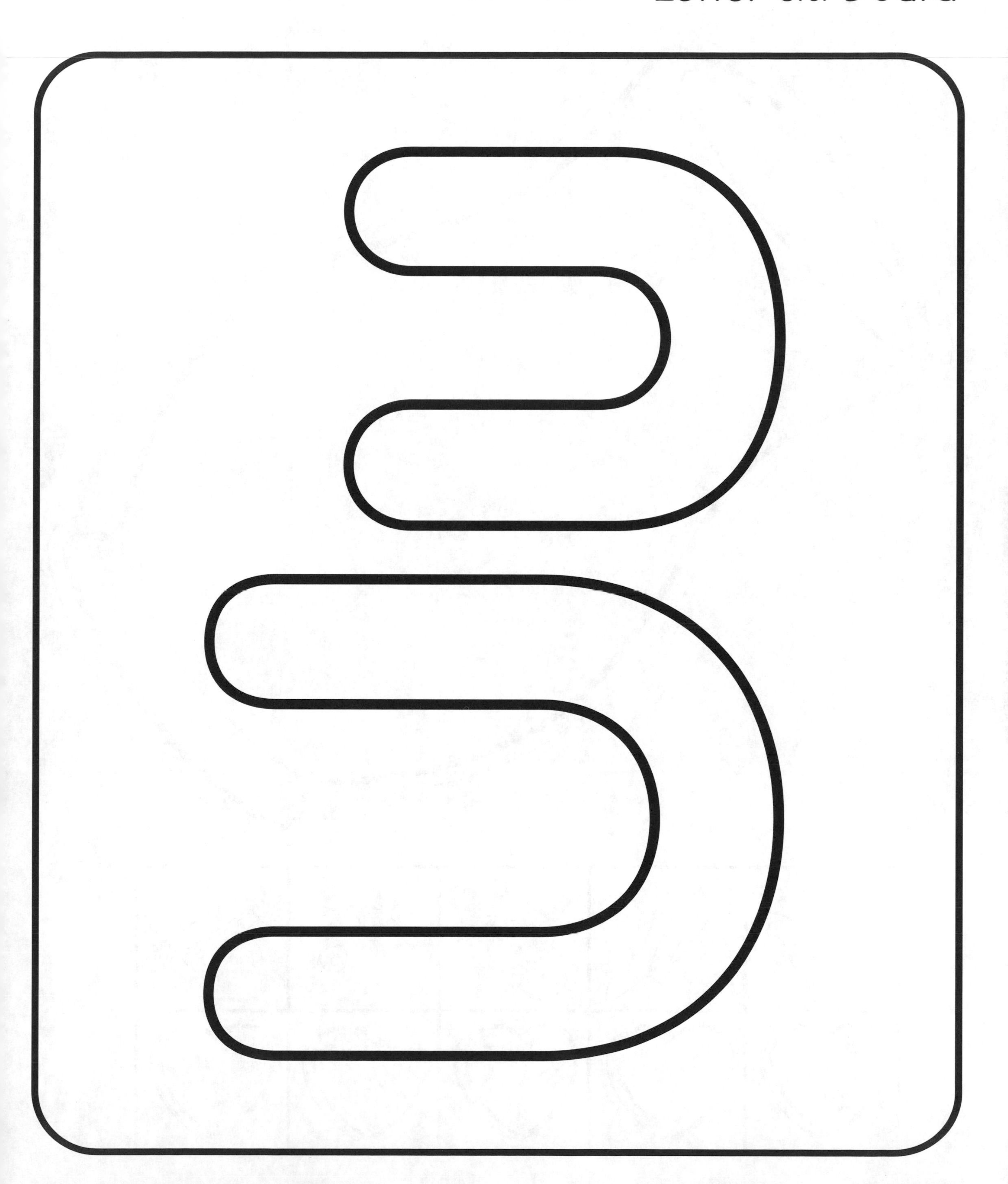

Letter Vv Pattern and Picture Squares

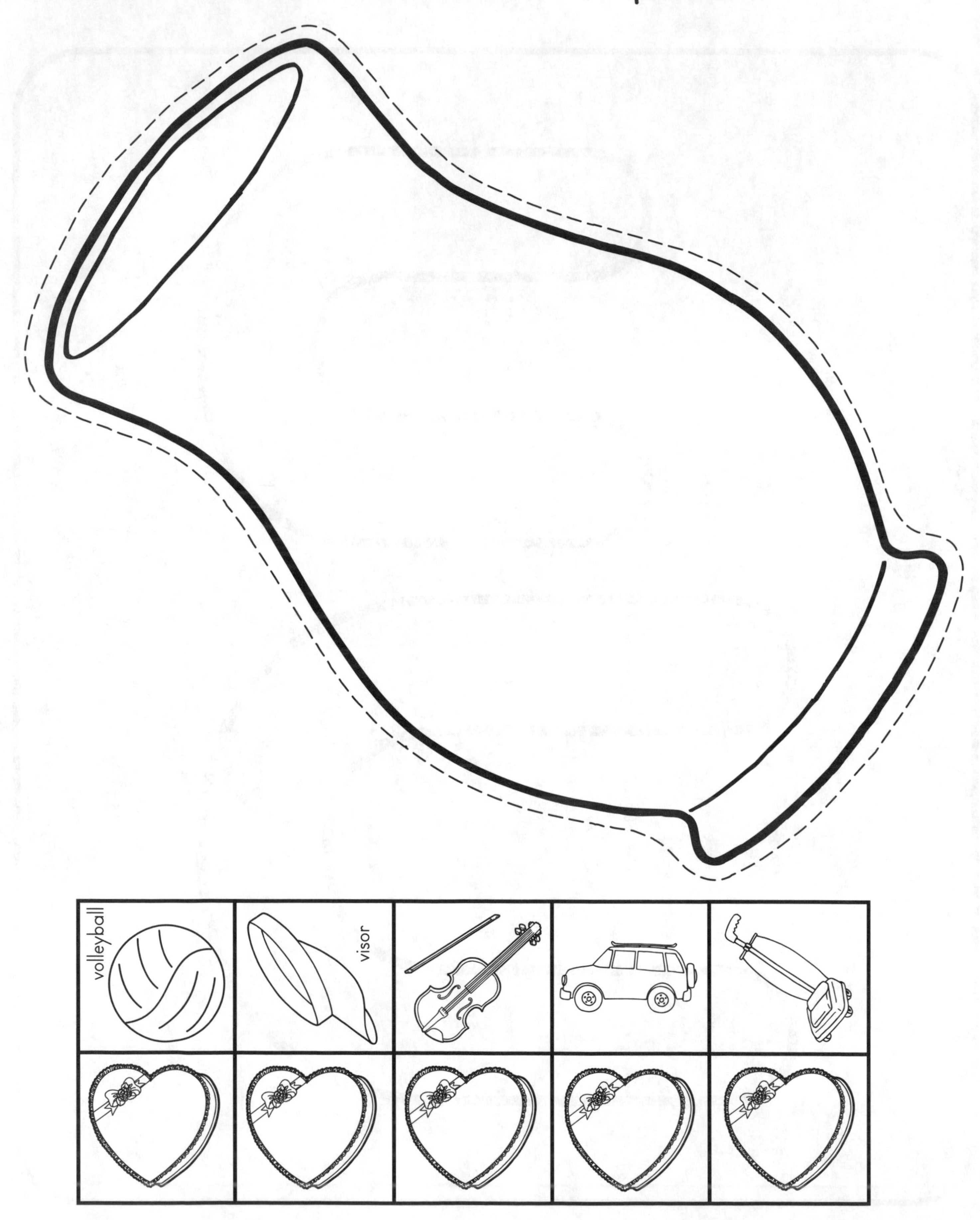

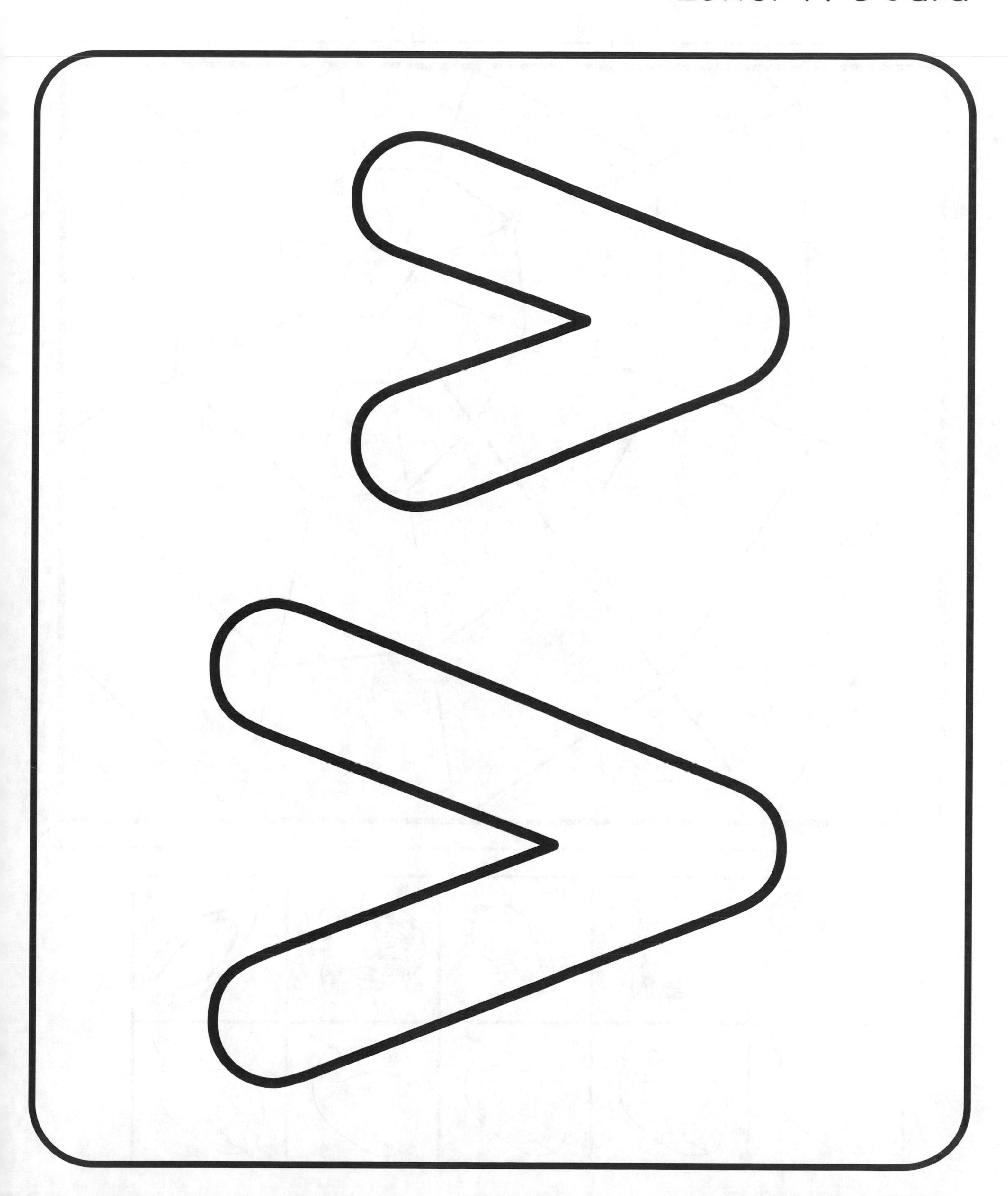

Letter Ww Pattern and Picture Squares

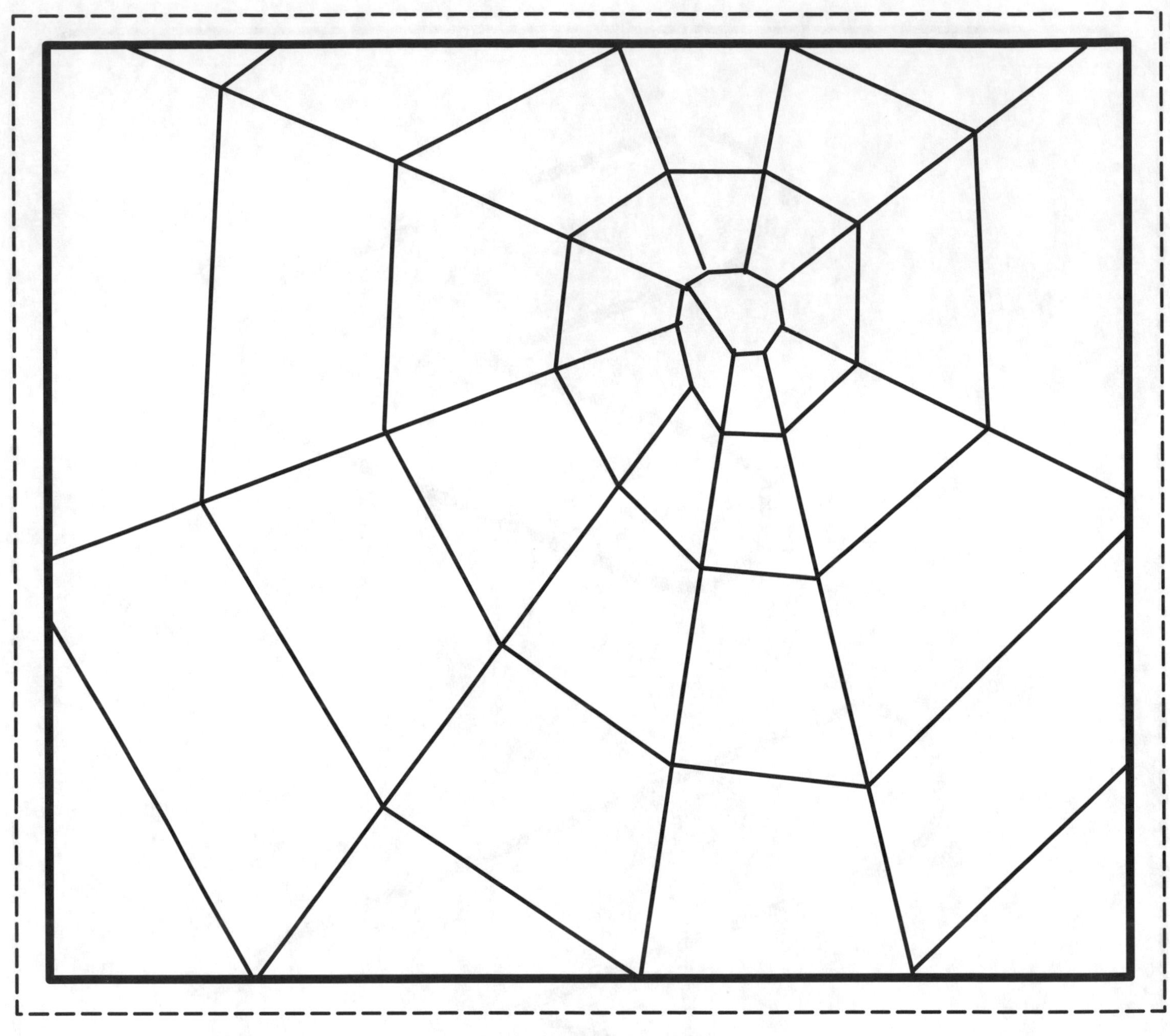

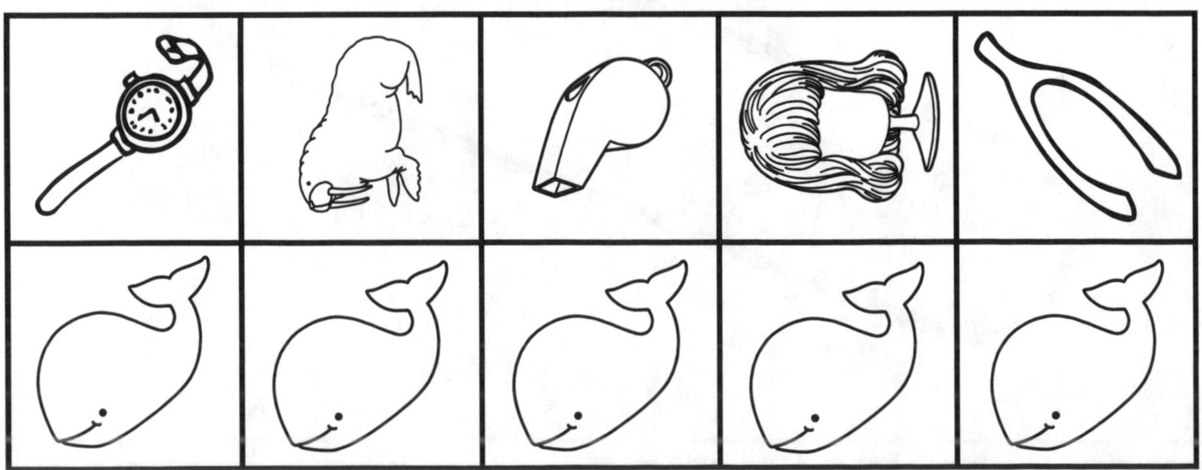

Letter Ww Board

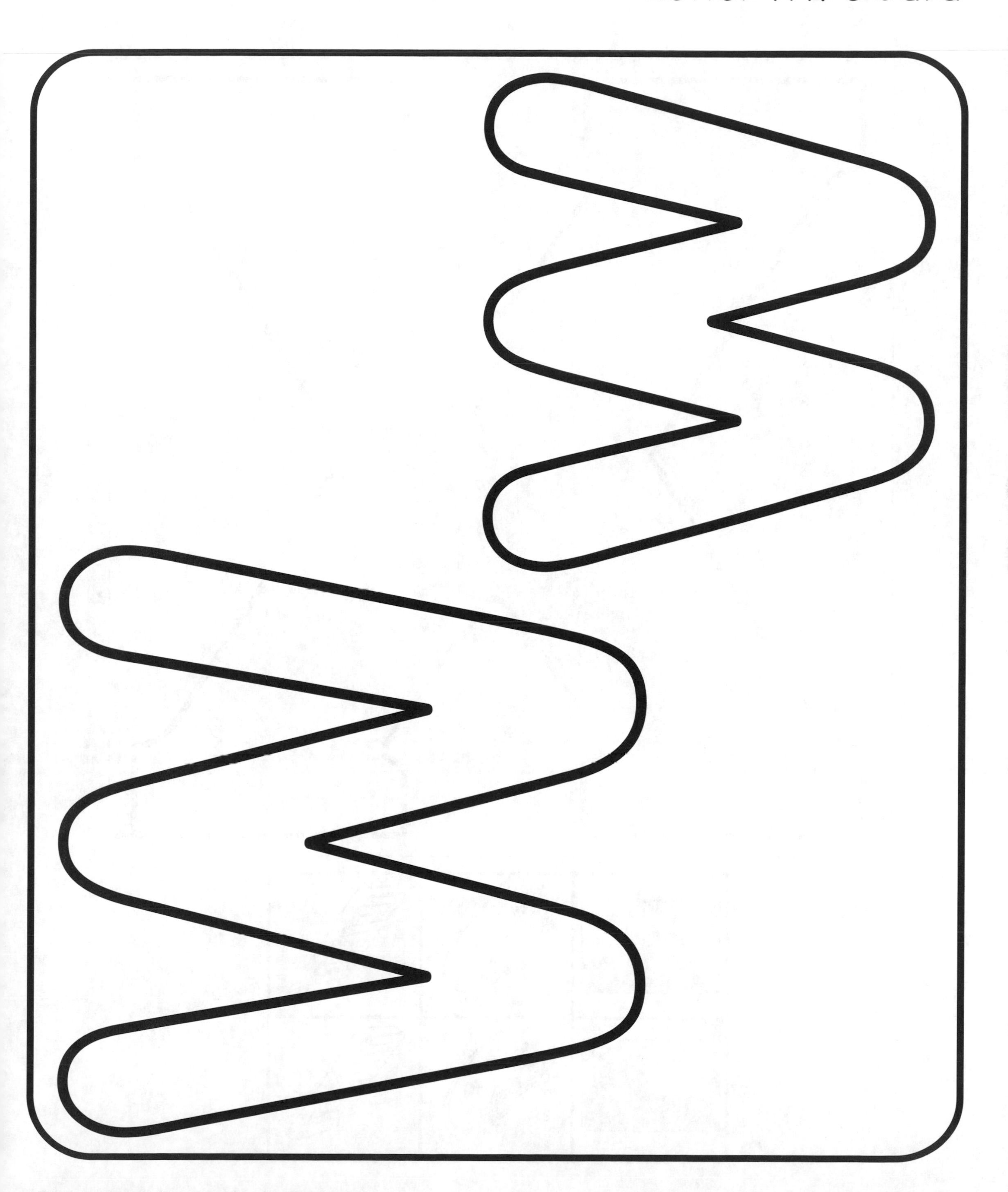

Letter Xx Pattern and Picture Squares

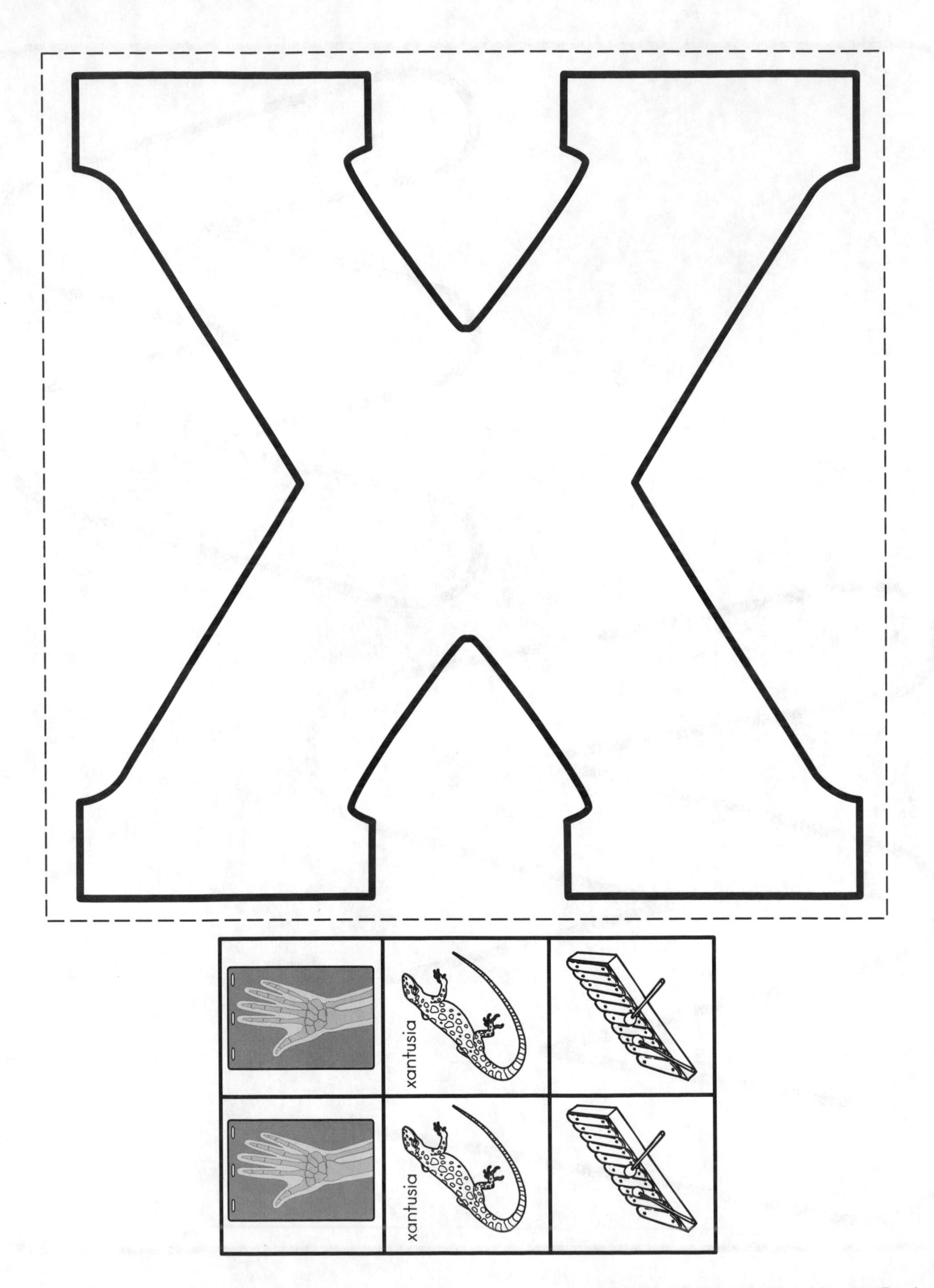

Letter Xx Board

Letter Yy Pattern and Picture Squares

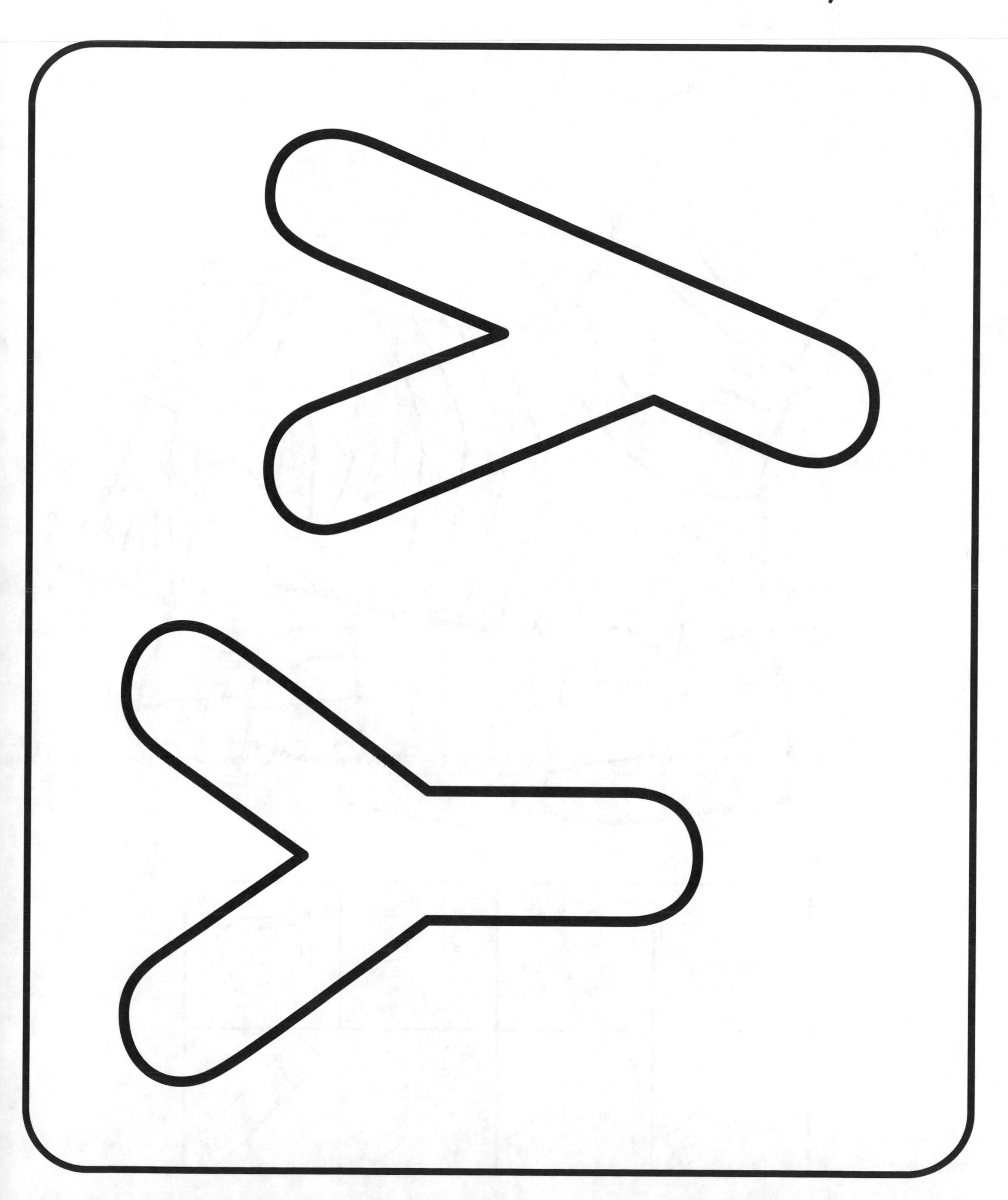

Letter Zz Pattern and Picture Squares

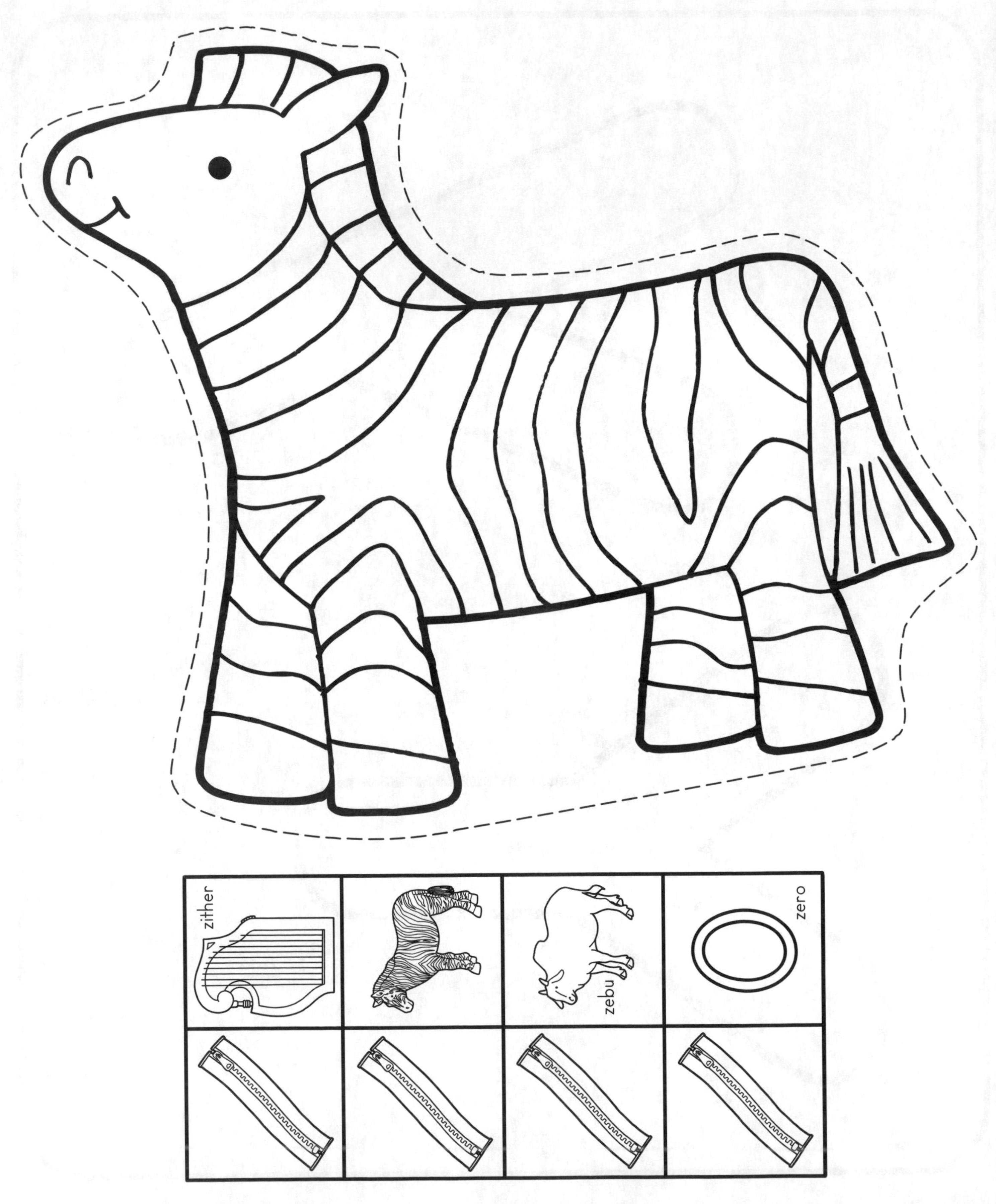

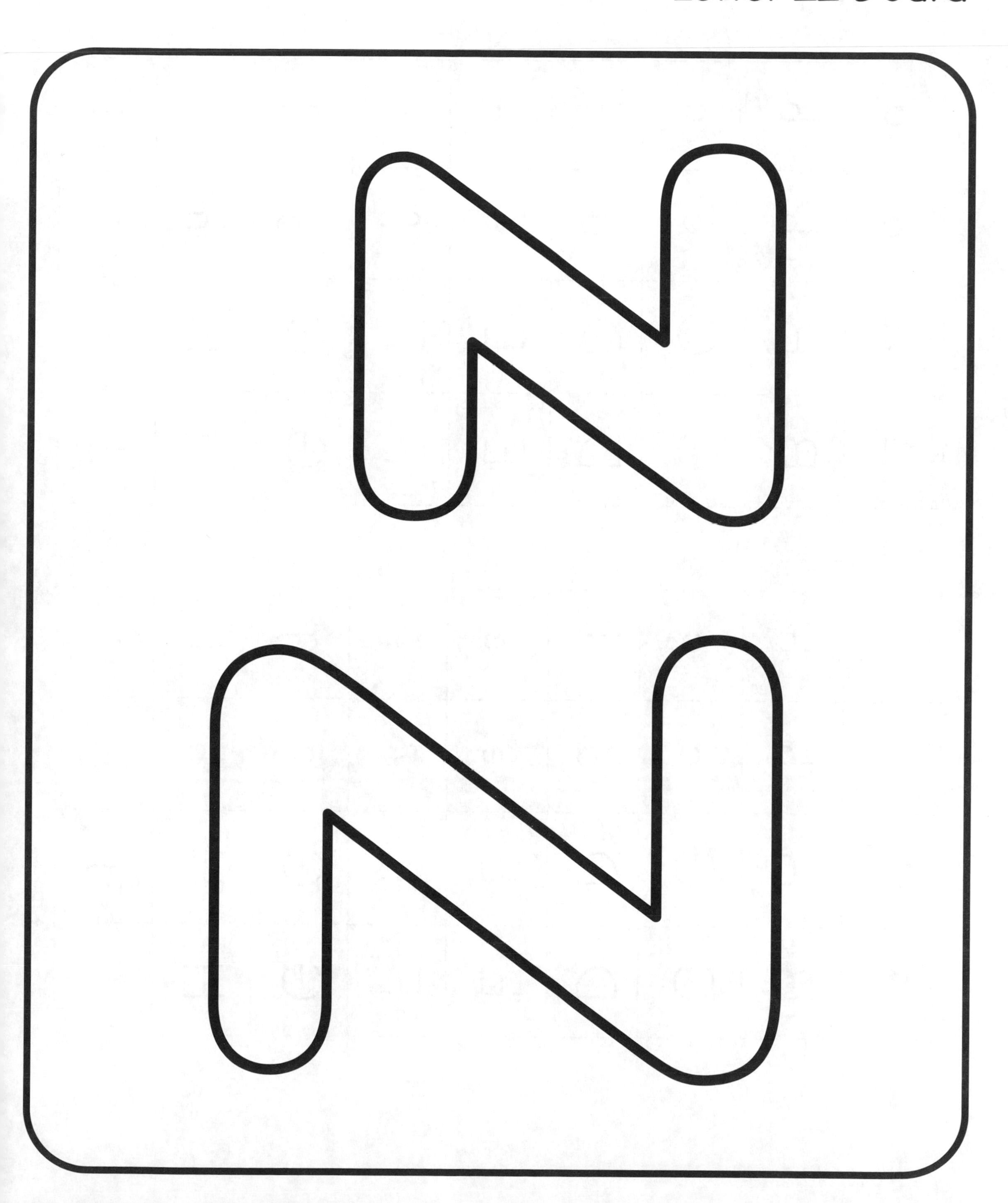

Letter Squares

a	b	c	d	e	f	g	h	i
a	b	c	d	e	f	g	h	i
A	B	C	D	E	F	G	H	I
A	B	C	D	E	F	G	H	I

a	b	c	d	e	f	g	h	i
a	b	c	d	e	f	g	h	i
A	B	C	D	E	F	G	H	I
A	B	C	D	E	F	G	H	I

Letter Squares

j	k	l	m	n	o	p	q	r
j	k	l	m	n	o	p	q	r
J	K	L	M	N	O	P	Q	R
J	K	L	M	N	O	P	Q	R

j	k	l	m	n	o	p	q	r
j	k	l	m	n	o	p	q	r
J	K	L	M	N	O	P	Q	R
J	K	L	M	N	O	P	Q	R

Letter Squares

s	t	u	v	w	x	y	z
s	t	u	v	w	x	y	z
S	T	U	V	W	X	Y	Z
S	T	U	V	W	X	Y	Z

s	t	u	v	w	x	y	z
s	t	u	v	w	x	y	z
S	T	U	V	W	X	Y	Z
S	T	U	V	W	X	Y	Z